HANK WANGFORD

VOLUME III

THE MIDDLE YEARS

AS TOLD TO

DR SAM HUTT

Pan Original
PAN BOOKS

London, Sydney and Auckland

To my Mother and Sister, Jean Pateman and Elena Rothy.
With love and a big Hi! from Hank.

No characters in this book are fictitious.
Some names have been changed to protect the innocent
and preserve the guilty.

First published 1989 by Pan Books Ltd,
Cavaye Place, London SW10 9PG
9 8 7 6 5 4 3 2 1
© Sam Hutt $incere $tories 1989
by arrangement with Colonel Frank Wangford
Illustrations by John Castle, © Pan Books Ltd 1989
Text design by Peter Ward
ISBN 0 330 30925 0
Photoset by Parker Typesetting Service, Leicester
Reproduced, printed and bound in Great Britain by
BPCC Hazell Books Ltd, Member BPCC Ltd
Aylesbury, Bucks

CONTENTS

INTRODUCTION

FROM THE DESK OF COLONEL FRANK WANGFORD

I'm a man of few words so we're not going to keep you for long from reading this fine book. We just want to say how pleased and proud we are that PAN BOOKS and $INCERE $TORIES have come together to bring you this first volume in a series about our boy Hank.

There are some tough things said in this slim volume, but you don't need me to tell you that sometimes life is like that. It may seem that Hank is a bit of a loser, but after all a winner is only a loser in disguise. Maybe at times we seem hard on Hank financially, but if we gave him more money, he'd only spend it. Look at Elvis.

When you get to the end, remember that this is only the first in a series of five volumes, starting in the middle and working our way outwards. We are discussing with PAN BOOKS whether we can run a special offer on the next book and run two volumes into one. If Volume IV is the Eighties, with all the glamour of Hank's success, maybe we can offer you Volume II, the Sixties, entirely free. Two for the price of one. We shall see.

We at $INCERE $TORIES, where it's Better to Have Bad Taste than to Taste Bad, may be new in the world of publishing but we are beginning to like the word *Volume.* We hope you do too. Tell your friends.

Sincerely,

Col Frank Wangford

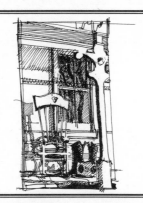

AUTHOR'S NOTE

I'm very happy the Colonel asked me to write this book on Hank. I'm very happy for all the help from Dillie Keane, Michael and Virginia Storey, Steve Wolfenden, Susie Harries, Caroline Arber, Paul Fitzgerald; Rachel Calder, Juliet Gardiner, all at $incere $tories – Peter and Sumi Jenner, Ian Richards – Hilary Davies and her Household Hints, and all at Pan Books. I'm specially indebted to Charlie and Gilly McKelvie who gave me the seclusion of Hilcot Farm, where I wrote most of this.

While some of the stories in here may seem like back-tracking, and outside the scope and era covered by this volume, Colonel Frank himself suggested to me that a little taster here and there from other volumes in the Wangford Quintych would help to throw a bit of perspective on things. The Colonel is a past master at throwing perspectives should they be needed. He has decided that Hank's hagiographer adding some autobiographical details can only enrich the total picture, and accepts that Hank and I are for ever inextricably involved. He no longer treats any personal memoirs as self-indulgence.

He may not be able to define it exactly, but he knows that with Hank and me we are talking *symbiosis* here.

Sam Hutt

A Sincere
☆
Fifty Per Cent

The following is a tape transcript of a meeting on 20 August 1987 with Hank Wangford and his personal manager, Colonel Frank Wangford, at his central office in Arizona. Sincere Management has given us permission to reprint it verbatim as an introduction to Hank and the Colonel.

© *The Sincere Trust*

SAM: We're here today to meet with Colonel Frank Wangford to discuss a book he is commissioning me to write about his client Hank Wangford. We're expecting Hank himself to arrive in the Colonel's inner sanctum, his suite here at the Bright Angel Lodge on the rim of the Grand Canyon. The view is quite magnificent, a fit setting for this unique opportunity to meet these unique men. Thank you, Colonel.

COL. FRANK: **What's the deal?**

SAM: No deal, Colonel, we just want to talk to you.

COL. FRANK: **What do you mean, there's no deal? There's always a deal. What's my fee?**

SAM: But, Colonel, you asked *me* here so you could say your piece. *You've hired me. I* get the fee.

COL. FRANK: **But that's impossible. I always get the fee. Where's the contract?**

SAM: Look, I haven't got the contract here, but I don't need it because you hired me to write a book about your boy Hank. So I've come here to interview you.

1

COL. FRANK: **Sorry, no interviews. You'll have to go. I only do interviews by post. Postal only.**

SAM: This is for *your* book about Hank. This is for the book you've hired me to write. I'm Sam Hutt, remember? Jesus.

COL. FRANK: **Ah, oh, yes, of course. I remember now. Well, you're welcome, son. What do you want to know?**

SAM: I'd like to talk about you and Hank. We'd like to know about your relationship.

COL. FRANK: **Me and Hank? Well, it's like father and son, I guess. He *leans* on me a lot and needs *advice and direction* from me at times. All it takes is just a little nudge mostly, but occasionally I have to be a bit firm.**

SAM: How firm?

COL. FRANK: **Well, you know, just hold him by the elbow and *persuade* him a little. Nothing heavy. We don't need to anyway because Hank trusts me. He trusts me totally. See, I told you, it's a father-son relationship. *He comes to me.* I don't have to spy on him or anything. He's a good boy.**

SAM: What does Hank come to you for? Business advice? Creative input?

COL. FRANK: **Yeah, you see, all of that. Naturally, I handle his business affairs because he has no idea how to organize himself. Creative stuff? Well, now, I don't want to—**

SAM: Did you write songs with him, or collaborate on any of the stage shows?

COL. FRANK: **Now, all the stage shows and spectaculars and such are part of Volume IV, so we'll talk about that in the next book, and as for songs, well, we don't really want to take anything away from Hank's achievements. Let him take all the glory. That's fine. That's why he gets up on stage. Let's just say *I was always there* when he needed me. That's something Hank doesn't always seem to acknowledge.**

SAM: What do you mean?

COL. FRANK: **Well, I don't want to start running my boy down, but you see, Hank is very *mean*, you know, very tight-fisted, a little too interested in money for his own good. Instead of concentrating on all the artistic stuff like writing and performing, he wants to know *details*. Where the money comes from, tax, what expenses he's going to get and stuff like that. I tell him that's what he pays *me* for. Mind you, he pays me little enough, I don't know why I do it. Some gratitude would help now and then, but what the hell. I'm just too indulgent. And Hank seems to want the money *and* the glory. And he won't budge. He seems to think for some reason he deserves a whacking fifty per cent, *yep, a fifty-per-cent share of everything he earns. Every goddam thing.* Can you believe** that? All we get is what's left, and *we have all the expenses.* All the office work, the phone calls, the meetings, all of that, and he has none of it. Just a full fifty per cent of every single minutest thing he does, every last bit of it. All that money for himself. *Just to have fun.* While I work on and have all the aggravation. Hell, he *enjoys* getting up on stage, it's not even like work to him. I'm the one who has to slog. So you can understand it's a sore point with me, and, like I said, Hank just isn't prepared to budge.

SAM: But isn't fifty per cent a lot for *you* to take?

COL. FRANK: Well, you see, we're a partnership and, unless there's something strange going on, partnerships are fifty-fifty. Without my help Hank couldn't possibly have made it. He knows that. When I met him in Seattle, he was in a terrible state. Playing with this bunch of loser wetbacks. He'd even married his lead singer. I warned him not to mix business with business but there you go. He's always been a fool for the women, and a marrying fool at that. Hell, if he had even more of a cut he'd just get married again and pay out even more alimony.

SAM: OK, let's talk about you, Colonel. Why do you live here? It's quite isolated, especially from the business community you work with so closely. Can you keep in touch with them and with Hank from here?

COL. FRANK: No problem. I don't have to tell you about faxes and modems. We keep in touch, rest assured. A little ... *delegation* ... now and then, but we know what's going on. That's what ears and eyes are for.

SAM: But why are you out here?

COL. FRANK: Well, I've been here at Bright Angel for near on ten years now. Why choose here? Just look out of that window, there's the answer. The Canyon. Look at it, isn't it beautiful? God's Great Slice. The big one. I love it. I like to wake up every morning and *look out at the biggest slice anybody ever took out of anything.* Keeps me going. It's inspirational.

SAM: And it's here, by The Great Slice, that you built the Sincere Empire.

COL. FRANK: Yep. This is where it all started, and it *is* quite an empire now, isn't it? Well, here's where the partnership comes in again, because it was Hank who first thought up the name and a lot of the slogans. He started it with *$INCERE PRODUCTS*, the makers of the only Genuine Reproduction Hank Wangford products. Brought to you with *Absolutely No Regard to Quality.* Then came *$INCERE $ONGS, No Pay, No Play.* That's one of my slogans, pleased with that. Anyhow, our publishing house is now working closely with Warner Chappell International Music.

Then there was *$INCERE $PECTACULARS*, for making films and TV and theatre shows. Things like CHAP, the Manchester

Christmas Prison gig on TV, RADIO WANG. *$INCERE $OUNDS, Our Heart on Your Sleeve*, is our recording company. *$INCERE $TORIES*, for book publishing. Now, all of these come under the umbrella of *THE $INCERE TRU$T*, where *Integrity is Integral*; it is something absolutely fundamental to our whole philosophy of things. Currently we're interested in moving into insurance, a very solid area, with *$INCERE $ECURITIES*, where *We Make Your Money*. If it was good enough for the Grand Ol' Opry ... So with all of this riding on the book, you understand why I need to check you out.

SAM: What do you mean? I thought it was all agreed?

COL. FRANK: **Sure, sure, but I'm just checking you're *qualified* to write this. I've heard you're some kind of doctor, right? Though, by the look of you, you must be some weird kind of doctor. You seem more like a hippie to me. As a matter of fact you look a bit like Hank without the moustache. So what kind of doctoring do you do, and how come you go around looking the way you do?**

SAM: That's just how I look. I can't go around with a mirror stuck on my forehead just to prove I'm a doctor. I do clinical work in Women's Health Care.

COL. FRANK: **But you are a doctor, not a writer, right?**

SAM: Yes, but so what? Writing's not that difficult.

COL. FRANK: **Huh, so you're not a real writer. Hmm ... Do you know anything about Hank's music? Or Country music at all?**

SAM: Quite a lot. I'm a musician myself and I started in Country music long before I met Hank.

COL. FRANK: **When did you meet Hank? I was going to introduce you to him today. He should be here any time now.**

SAM: We're old friends, and it's because I already know him so well that I'm the best one to ghost his story. I got to know him in Suffolk in the late Seventies, when he'd come back to England. You weren't around then.

COL. FRANK: **Oh, then. Yes, I lost touch with him for a while. He had been very difficult, you know, tantrums and all that. He said he wanted to leave the American music scene. Said something about sincerity and how it smelt bad. But if the music sells, where's the problem? It's the money that we don't want devalued.**

SAM: Colonel, with all respect, music isn't only money.

COL. FRANK: **That's easy for you to say. You don't have to exist on fifty per cent ... Anyway, you say you're a musician as well as a doctor and that you like Country music ... Do you perform as well?**

4

SAM: I certainly do. I didn't want to tell you this, but as we're going to be working together you ought to know. In that time you lost touch with Hank I started playing in his band. I even stood in for him a few times when he got what you called *difficult*.

COL. FRANK: **You did WHAAT? Why wasn't I told? Did you get paid? How did the gigs go? Where's the commission?**

SAM: Well, I'm telling you now. The gigs went well. I had a bit of a problem with the American accent but no one noticed.

COL. FRANK: **Hmmm. Do you drink, do you booze a lot?**

SAM: Very little. I don't like being drunk.

COL. FRANK: **Hmm. And you *are* a real doctor?**

SAM: One hundred per cent, Colonel. Guaranteed. Though I spend more time on music.

COL. FRANK: **Hmm. Interesting. You *do* look like Hank now I can see you a bit closer. Hmmm. Have you got a management deal? Maybe we can—**

VOICE ON INTERCOM: Hank here for you Colonel.

COL. FRANK: **Show him in. Well, Sam, it's been very interesting meeting with you. Let's just keep that last bit to ourselves, OK? We'll talk about it another time.**

HANK: *Hello, Colonel. Hey, Sam, how're you doing? So is that right, you're going to write this book about me?*

SAM: Yes, the Colonel wants me to write your story. Is that OK by you?

HANK: *No problem. You'll be fine. You know me as well as anyone and you're not stupid. Hell, you're a medical man.*

COL. FRANK: **That's right, Hank. You should listen to him about your drinking. You're looking pretty rough right now. Can't you do anything for him, doc?**

HANK: *Come on, Colonel, lay off, will you? I've just got here. Let's talk about the book.*

COL. FRANK: **OK. I'm just worrying about *you*, Hank. You know I've got your best interests at heart.**

HANK: *Oh, yeah? Listen, Colonel, my best interests are what you make when you put my money in your bank account. And don't start that crap about being like a father to me, I'll be sick.*

SAM: Now, come on you guys, leave it alone, will you? We've got things to talk about.

HANK: *Right. OK. Let me tell you straight away that I'm real pleased that you're writing it because you understand.*

SAM: What do you mean?

HANK: *You know what I've been going on about, you know about love and hate and love and laughter. Real Country & Western stuff.*

SAM: You mean laughing at the things you love? That laughing at the sweet irony of things enhances rather than diminishes those things?

HANK: *Well, you've got something of it there. But then I guess my problem is always being taken for a clown, because I fool around so much.*

SAM: It's good to laugh and cry at the same time . . .

HANK: *You see, that's what I mean. You understand what I feel. Almost like we were brothers.*

COL. FRANK: **But you don't drink.**

SAM: That's true, Colonel, but check my teeth out, look here.

COL. FRANK: **Let's see ... Jeesus K. Rist, will you look at that gap! You've got the same kind of gap as Hank.**

HANK: *Look closer, Colonel. It's* exactly the same.

COL. FRANK: **Good grief, you're right. Looks like you've only got two front teeth, just like Hank.**

SAM: That's right. We were both born with only two incisors, the front teeth between the canines. David Bowie has prominent canines and hasn't he done well?

HANK: *The Doc here tells me that it's a one-in-four-hundred chance to have teeth like these, so it's got to be a million to one for both of us to have them. Strange, huh?*

COL. FRANK: **Now I look at you properly, Doctor, I can see how alike you are. Hmmm ... Listen, there's a couple of long distance calls I've gotta make, so you guys keep talking. I'll see you later.**

SAM: I still find our teeth really odd. But they make it easier for me to stand in for you on stage. I wonder if people notice the times it's me and not you—?

HANK: *I don't think so. I'm sure no one will be able to figure out who did what bits in those TV shows of ours. Hell, it looks like the Colonel hasn't even noticed you after all these years.*

Do you remember when I came back to Wangford? When I came back from America? It was a pretty strange home-coming for me, but when I came into the pub that night I saw you and I could see you were going through even harder times than I was. You were hunched over the bar, staring into a glass of beer like it was a crystal ball. You looked like the classic Country and Western loser, like the guy in 'Empty Bottle, Broken Heart and You're Still On My Mind'.

I guess I felt sorry for you, not because you'd gone through some kinda hard time, 'cos we all get that. More because I could see you were trying to drown your sorrows, to get away from them; and it doesn't work. The beer is never as bitter as the tears that you've still got to cry. That's why I thought I'd break in on your misery and check you out, and that's when I saw your face.

And the teeth, spitting image. Certainly was a shock.

That and being back in Wangford after such a long time must've set me up ready for it, but seeing someone as strung out as you were just flipped me into an entirely new frame of mind. Made me feel a bit like a father or a teacher of some kind, as if I had been somewhere you were heading for and I'd survived. I had to help you. I had to point a finger at the moon, to let you know that nothing is that bad. But that's what Country music is about, letting you know someone has been there before, that if you think you're low, how about this one. 'At Least I Know How to Stand on My Own Two Knees', 'I'll Be Over You When the Grass Grows Over Me', all of that. And if you've got troubles, someone's had it worse, we have to hold on to that. Country has an irony that laughs at itself, which is one of the reasons we both love the stuff.

Brits get very hung up about it being redneck, as if it's kind of right-wing, fascist stuff. Sure, some of it has that element, but that's not all it is. Hell, there may be a Moral Majority over there, and if you write a crap song like 'God Bless the USA' it's bound to be voted Country Song of the Year, but there's still a huge Immoral Minority, praise the Lord. They even used to be ashamed of the hick, hillbilly, redneck, poor-white-trash side of C & W in Nashville fer Chrissakes. They'd forgotten that like the Blues, it taps right into our raw emotions, goes straight for the heart. And the jugular sometimes. But it's the music of Survival, Country music. Some Brits think it's self-indulgent, which it may well be, but then they think it's self-indulgent to even cry. Damn their stiff upper lip, damn it to hell.

Anyway, I felt all this just in seeing you, without saying a single word. You looked like me, but not quite so far down the road.

SAM: So you had me sussed even before buying me a beer?

HANK: *Any jilted fool could see what you were putting yourself through, it was written all over your face. You were wallowing in it, like a pig in shit. But there's nothing wrong with that, it's just you were wallowing in the wrong shit, fooling yourself, missing the point. You told me you were feeling sorry for yourself because out of the blue, with no provo-cation, your girl goes and marries your old flat mate. Serious C & W. No provocation? I know you too well, Doc. What was it? Other women? Didn't want kids? I'm sure she had good reason to go. You were probably just an asshole.*

SAM: (Indistinct)

HANK: *So are they all OK now? You said they had kids. You're friends?*

SAM: Yes, sure we are, of course, no other way. And they're fine, with three lovely kids, and we're all very good friends. And it had to happen that way.

HANK: *Yes, but you never realise that at the time, do you? So, life goes on, cry a few tears, huh? No, you were settling into Self-Pity City. You'd got your mortgage already.*

SAM: All right. What do you think the Colonel *really* wants in the book?

HANK: *Oh, to hell with what the Colonel wants, I want an honest book. I'd like a lot about our relationship, so I think we need a fair bit about you.*

SAM: Well, I think the Colonel wants some kind of pop biog. but if we're going to be honest, we'll have to tell all about those months and even years I've stood in for you. So maybe, although the book is about you, I could start with myself doctoring out in Canada. Then move on to the very first time I saw you in Vancouver.

HANK: *That sounds fine. But listen, Doc, I've got something on my mind here that won't go away so I've got to ask it before we start. Is that stuff about teeth and how alike we look all a load of hooey? I mean, well, look Sam . . . Are You Me? Am I you, are we one and the same? Is this all bullshit?*

SAM: What the hell are you going on about? *Me You?* Ha, piece of shite – of course I'm not you. I mean, is Clark Kent Superman? Or what about Peter Parker, is he Spiderman? Come on, Hank, you're way off target. Are you starting to believe your own publicity? You really *want to think of yourself as a singing gynaecologist?* You enjoy all those seedy, slavering journalists asking you about whether you're *still keeping your hand in*, ho ho, nudge nudge? You really like all that crap? Can't you just play the music and leave me quietly to be the doctor? Well, if that's what you want, you can keep it and fuck right off and be famous in your own time. Just let me do the gigs and play the music.

HANK: *OK, OK, OK. I'm sorry . . . I just had to ask, that's all. It was on my mind and I needed to clear it up . . .*

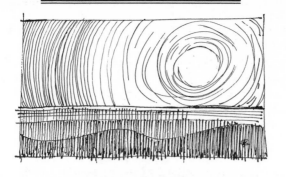

Gone West,
☆
or Northern Comfort

People always warn you against the Prairies. *Too flat*, they tell you, as if to prepare you for the worst. It's like whispering confidentially in your ear that the sea is full of waves, or that France is a bit on the French side. Still they assume that no one is ready for the Flatlands, and that's how it was when I went for the job.

My mother had seen an ad in the paper which said with an edge of desperation about it *ANY DOCTOR – SASKATCHEWAN . . . ANY DOCTOR*, it had an undiscerning ring I found irresistible and my name was written all over it. As it happens, at that time, I had itchy feet. I had always felt equivocal about being a doctor through my years of study and even since I had qualified and registered a couple of years before. Although I had a General Practice among the Alternative or Underground society of the late Sixties and was with *my people*, I still felt uneasy. Private medicine, and having to charge fees, stuck in my craw. Visiting American rock stars would come to see me when they were ill because I was *Doctor Sam*. I thought people only wanted to know me because I was a doctor. My first and only identity crisis. It became sycophantic and I got sick of it. The only thing keeping me in London was the delightful work I was doing with Doctor Blackie, the Queen's Homeopath, who was teaching me the beginnings of the subtle art of Homeopathy.

So when she saw this ad for someone to work for a few months running a general practice single-handed with its own hospital out in

9

the middle of the Prairies, my mother phoned me and I was off like a shot to a desirable little mews property at the Range Rover end of the Portobello Road with the fire of the wilderness raging in my eyes. A healthy young doctor, probably a climbing type just back from doing Everest with no oxygen *and holding his breath for the last hundred feet*, tried to calm me down by telling me just how flat the bottom line really was. But I was babbling on so about Western movies and Country songs that he felt I had to be brought down to earth and kept saying that the Prairies were Only Flat; no mountains, no hills, in fact *No Scenery*. Now, I'm a big mountain fan, but had he never seen the horizon holding up the sky, and had his eyes never rolled up at the beauty of the Great Vault above? No, he had to warn me not to expect anything exciting, it would be really *boring*.

And on that first day, as I drove out from Saskatoon through the yellow seas of rape and corn, I didn't expect to see the silver, onion-shaped dome spires of the Kremlin glinting on the Canadian horizon. It was 140 miles to little Rose Valley but when I was less than half-way there I could see that the Russians had got here long before me. In fact they were Ukrainians who came over in the early twentieth century for the Prairie Population. Shiploads of them were brought over free and given ten dollars and a quarter (160 acres) of land to farm. So they brought their churches, and when they had torn down the forest with their bare hands and cleared the trees and made the land into cornfields, they praised the Lord under their silver and gold domes which shone out into God's Great Blue above them. And so did the Norwegians who came up from Minnesota looking for somewhere even flatter and colder. And so did the French, the English, the Irish and the Scots. Not the Saulteaux Indians, though, who'd had their own Prairie Population a few centuries before and weren't too keen on pulling up the trees.

I didn't know any of this at the time as I sped through the cornfields with the outgoing doctor and he wasn't about to tell me much.

'See Ruby, she'll tell you,' he said to everything in a surly, medical sort of way. Occasionally he glanced at my henna'd hair. The long, flowing chestnut tresses didn't seem to faze him. Maybe they made him homesick. He certainly wasn't worried whether I was a Hippie or an axe murderer as long as I had the paper with the qualifications on it.

So I fell silent and looked at that straight line slicing round me, golden yellow underneath and the brightest blue above. They don't come more primary, I thought. And I thought of the lazy days off ahead, cruising through the yellow in the good doctor's silver Cadillac, pulling a wake of shivering cornheads behind me as I streaked down the long, straight grid roads right into the sun. Just dreaming, though, for that was the one and only trip in the Caddy because waiting for me in Rose Valley was a matchbox-sized Mazda the good doctor had hired from

Dial-a-Dat that put paid to Kerouac visions of Cadillac heroics. Smallest of the small, it was not quite big enough for a fully grown Japanese person, and with the slipstream of a gnat and a motor to match, it was not going to cause much of a ripple or even a rustle in the great sea of grain.

The man back in London had warned me though. He said it would be flat and boring, so I'd only got myself to blame. And Dial-a-Dat is what you'd expect from a doctor who was going back to India to get a wife.

That's what was happening. Dr Datta was taking time off to go back home, find a wife, arrange the wedding and bring her back to the Saskatchewan plains to look after him. Just like that. So the good doctor was taking me to Rose Valley to show me his practice, see the hospital and meet and greet some of the folks I was going to work with, and to tour the town. And meet Ruby, his medical secretary and receptionist, his right hand, his Mum Friday – there's one in every practice. Doctors wave their arms about and act like little boys to get their Rubies to mother them; no one's really taking advantage. Anyway, we did the Grand Tour in all of seventeen minutes with the doc on the run. He was a man ready to leave, On His Way, keen to be on the plane to go and find the wife. He grabbed his coat and hat and his briefcase and raced out of the door.

'See Ruby, she'll tell you.'

He was gone and I was left standing on the porch of his bungalow, dazed, knowing where I was coming from but not knowing quite where I was at. I looked round the house, a standard American wood-frame bungalow with rooms in it, a porch outside and a roof on the top.

Inside, it was entirely normal too. A full range of brown tones. A settee or a sofa, one of the two. A bed in the bedroom and a mirror right over the washbasin in the bathroom so you could watch yourself shave. A kitchen with a fridge, a sink, a cooker and cupboards. No frills. It was like lodgings, the married quarters annexe to the hospital. It made me want to hang furry dice all over or drape it all with whatever the equivalent of a leopard-skin steering-wheel cover is for furniture. But the good doc had his priorities right. He'd kept the car. A wise man. I smiled. 'You can have my House but please don't Mess with my Car.' I'd do the same, I thought, heading for the porch. You can't drive a living-room off the road, you can't get drunk and crash it. You can *trash* it, sure, but the good doc would have figured out that he'd be back with the wife before cabin fever – the Prairie shakes – hit the Hippie Doctor too hard.

The clatter of the flyscreen door behind me as I came out on to the porch suddenly brought me back to earth. *Clatter*. I had got there, I was in the West. As I turned and looked at the screen door still flapping gently the Images came tumbling out.

Cowboys in the night, a face through the screen.
Bart don't live here any more.
Leave us alone, won'tcha? We don't know nothing.
We ain't seen no masked riders.
We just farm the land here.

Clatter. And this was to be my porch for the next few months. It had a rocking chair on it and the whole thing was encased in heavy-duty netting which I didn't really appreciate until my first encounter with Saskatchewan's summer skeeters, which were more like helicopters than mosquitoes, rumbling out of the gloaming at the first whiff of blood. The porch faced west and, standing there, I knew I was in for a few good sunsets; looking through the dust that still hung in the air from the good doc's getaway down the dirt road and past a couple of jackpines on the other side of the road, I could see the makings of a fine welcome gathering in the reddening sky. As a serious Hippie, sunsets were important to me and watching the fire smouldering in the west I could tell I'd come to the right place.

Clatter. The screen door was still flapping and as I looked back through it I saw a big old radio sitting there. I reached in through the doorway and switched it on. A short sweep of the tuner got me straight on to Radio Des Moines, Iowa, a country station with Ernest Tubb telling us why he was 'Too Old To Cut The Mustard'. I let the screen door clatter once more as I went back out on to the porch and settled into the old rocking chair. As Buck Owens came on the radio with 'I Wouldn't Live In New York City (If You Gave Me the Whole Dang Town)', I started to drift off and my mind went blank. The sunset went all wobbly like an old movie flashback and I floated away. Suddenly I was back in my private London consulting rooms six months before, still struggling with my socialist scruples, working alone and of necessity charging fees for my services. But no matter how many Green Shield stamps I gave out or how many people I saw for nothing I couldn't buy off my sense of guilt.

I Saw the Light

My London consulting suite was in fact the living-room of the flat I shared with two friends, Jenny Fabian who had written *Groupie*, a classic Sixties' account of life inside rock stars' jeans, and Roger Chapman the lead singer with the great British rock group Family. Roger had a bizarre quavering voice unlike any other, and was also (apart from Bertolt Brecht) the first man I ever saw with designer stubble. A true original, a man way before his time.

A Fred Neil record was playing, which was not really surprising as I was playing a lot of his music at that time. I liked his long, rambling bittersweet songs and deep, cracked voice. Fred Neil was a sort of Folkie who lived in Florida, and would come up north to the Big City, and record a lot of very stoned tracks. Inside those sprawling songs though, his voice, naturally low and rumbling, had a tender rawness that hit at my heart. His songs often teetered on the edge of incoherence, but then so did a lot of people in 1970. 'The Dolphins' was a gem, a wistful little sketch of yearning and lost love. Another classic was 'Everybody's Talking', the theme music from *Midnight Cowboy*. The song is the story of Fred's difficulties in coping with the Big City.

Most of us have our Fred Neils, our personal esoteric favourites. And because they are our own personal favourites, we think we *own* them. We become possessive and welcome any interest resentfully. We like showing off our little discoveries, we love *introducing* people to them. But we don't really like anyone to be presumptuous enough to have heard *our* Senegalese singer, seen *our* Chilean film before *we've* told them about it. Many people, like some of the Folkies of the Fifties and many die-hard Country and Western fans, are possessive over whole styles of music. These people often turn out to be the purists who tell us *how* the music is to be played and how any deviation from the original is an unforgivable contamination.

As I sat at my desk looking intelligently thoughtful and scratching at a sheet of paper, head in hand the way they teach you to do in medical school, a couple came into the room to see the doc. They were both American and had the tatty glamour of rock stars. She was blonde and pretty and wore tight jeans and cowboy boots. The guy had long, dark hair and long, dark eyebrows knotted over his eyes full of a dampened intensity, was wearing a brown suede jacket with Indian symbols over it and a scarf or two tied round his neck. He heard the music and said

'Hey, that's Freddie Neil.'

I twisted around with a mixture of delight and dismay.

'How do you know Fred Neil?'

Who does he think he is? What's he doing on my patch?

'Know him? I *played* with him.'

'You *played* with Fred Neil?' I was floundering a bit. 'What's your name?'

'Gram Parsons.'

Gram Parsons. *GRAM PARSONS* . . . What a turn up. As it happened, I had been listening a lot at that time to Parsons' album 'The Gilded Palace of Sin', his first with the Flying Burrito Brothers, the band he formed in the late Sixties after he left the Byrds. I was a Byrds fan from way back and had loved everything they recorded. Everything that is until they did 'Sweetheart of the Rodeo' in 1968. I hated it. It was far too close to pure Country for me and I was *not* a Country fan in any way. I associated it with Folk and had never realized that my old love, the Everly Brothers, were Country through and through. The record, 'Sweetheart', had been a result of the Byrds being taken down a few Country byways and highways by Gram. There were none of the old chiming, zinging Rickenbacker twelve-string guitars, the backwards tapes, the soaring harmonies or brain-damaged songs like 'Mind Gardens' or 'Everybody's Been Burned'.

As a child of the Sixties, I was deeply distressed.

When Gram broke away from the Byrds I didn't see the band he formed, the Flying Burrito Brothers, as a Country band at all. Well, shoot ma dog, we're all kinda dumb at times, I guess. I thought the Burritos were great, I really liked their songs, and there seemed to be something quite emotional about the voices, but I didn't see them then as playing real Country in the same way as I thought the Byrds had done before. I know that hindsight's twenty-twenty, but I did realize how wrong I'd been, that, although the Burritos were rock musicians with a rock ethic, the music was firmly rooted in traditional Country values and styles. You never know, do you?

So when Gram came with his wife Gretchen to see me, the first thing he did after telling me how he had recorded with Fred Neil was pick up my old acoustic guitar. A copy of a Macaferri, the kind of guitar Django Reinhardt used to play, made in the Forties, it has a lovely, warm, bassy sound. Gram started to strum and sang 'Empty Bottle, Broken Heart and You're Still On My Mind', a real honky-tonk classic.

> *The jukebox is playing a honky-tonk song,*
> *One more I keep saying and then I'll go home.*
> *What good will it do me? I know what I'll find,*
> *An empty bottle, a broken heart,*
> *And you're still on my mind.*
>
> *The people are dancing and having their fun*
> *While I sit here thinking 'bout what you have done,*
> *To try and forget you I turn to the wine,*
> *An empty bottle, a broken heart,*
> *And you're still on my mind.*
>
> *Alone and forsaken, so blue I could cry,*
> *I just sit here drinking 'till the bottle runs dry.*
> *What good will it do me? I know what I'll find,*
> *An empty bottle, a broken heart,*
> *And you're still on my mind.*

© L. McDaniel

His imperfect voice, broken but soulful, cut right through to my heart and in a flash I SAW THE LIGHT. It might even have been a classic satori right there, a true revelation in the traditional Zen Buddhist style. Whoosh . . . Boff . . . There, staring me in the face, I felt the spirit of Country for the first time.

A sudden understanding. *So that's what it's all about . . .*

It's a sigh of relief really. The exhilaration of long-overdue recognition. I knew what made Saul want to change his name and, like him, I became the worst of things, God help us, a convert. Gram seemed pleased about this evangelical fervour he brought out in people. He obviously enjoyed proselytizing and had a deep-rooted love of Country. He knew he was charismatic and knew he was the one who had to show people the soul of Country music.

Then he played 'Image of Me', a very black Country song, and went deeper into the dark side of Country. Raw songs, songs of death and of love abused, of cheating and of booze, of poverty and pain. Songs of troubled times, dark, lonely nights and restless souls. It touched an open wound somehow, and it was like hearing the Blues for the first time.

Gram had left the Burritos and had come over to Europe while the dust settled. He had met the Rolling Stones before and was hanging out with Keith Richard. The Stones had got a Country influence from Gram in songs like 'Dear Doctor', 'Dead Flowers' and 'Honky-Tonk Women'. They wrote 'Wild Horses' for Gram.

So over the next six months he was up and down between France and London seeing Keith. He had a furnished rock-star house in Kensington. He hadn't been one of fourteen children living in a one-room sharecropper's shack. He was a rich boy born in Florida and brought up in Georgia and he could support his lifestyle with minimal Rock 'n' Roll earnings. But rich boys feel the pain as well, and rich boys *can* get the blues. And Gram got the blues. Like Hank Williams, he wrote and sang some of the saddest songs around, not afraid to dig deep into his own restless sorrow.

Once I was playing a bunch of Parsons' tracks to a prospective Scots bass player as an indication of the kind of stuff I enjoyed. After a few heavy songs like 'Hearts On Fire', 'Thousand Dollar Wedding' and 'Love Hurts', the bass player said "Och, can ye no cheer up fer Chrissakes?" as Gram cracked on suicidally about being jilted at the altar and the sheer misery that loving someone can bring.

Gram, like all of us in different ways, needed to know that he was needed. He was an extremist, though, and his need to know had to be expressed in grandiose terms. He would dangle himself over an edge, push himself over mentally or physically and see how far his loved ones would reach out to pull him back to safety. The further out he pushed himself, and the further they had to reach to save him was an expression of their love for him.

In the times he was in town we would often play together. He would play me lots of George Jones. Hearing George Jones for the first time was like hearing Ray Charles for the first time. Tension and breaking in both voices.

He loved my guitar and wanted to take it to France with him. He was going to leave his Martin but I wouldn't have it. The Martin was a much better instrument but I liked the sound of mine and was worried it might get trashed in some early morning madness. Tension and breaking in my guitar.

As we got to know each other a little better we found we were both Scorpios, and in those massively astrological times this felt like some kind of bond. There is supposed to be a blackness, a dark sexuality and a self-destructiveness associated with Scorpio. As a young boy, I had cut out a drawing of a scorpion from a magazine, and had pencilled in lines from its arched-tail sting to its head, a fanciful squirt of venom from its sting into its own eyes. Luckily no psychiatrist saw this at the time.

I had always associated one of Gram's songs, 'Hot Burrito No 1' from 'Gilded Palace of Sin' with a strong Scorpionic streak.

Alternatively self-lacerating and defiantly proud, also known as 'I'm your Toy, I'm your Old Boy', it has an old theme. It was not a little masochistic and wickedly manipulative. It said:

I taught you to do whatever it is you're doing out there with somebody else . . . But I'm OK . . . It doesn't bother me . . . doesn't bother me at all . . . Ha! Do what you like . . . Fuck who you like . . . I'm fine, I don't need you anymore . . . It doesn't bother me, I don't care . . .

Clatter. As I rocked gently on the chair, I could hear George Jones singing 'Things Have Gone To Pieces' through the swinging screen door. *Clatter.* I'm going to have to get that door fixed. Things came slowly back into focus as I realized I was back way out West. By now the Saskatchewan sunset was crackling and blazing across the horizon like a celestial forest fire. Some stratospheric clouds had slid high across the sky to give us Golden Shafts and the Gates of Heaven and just as the Cosmos was about to burst its banks and spill all over the Prairies there was a knock on the door.

Hallo
☆
Stranger

'Hi, I'm Martin, your next-door neighbour.' A very big man was standing at the door with his very big hand outstretched so I shook it. Not the knuckle crusher you'd expect, just a friendly squeeze. In his other hand was a pie. He pushed it toward me.

'Pumpkin pie from Shirley and me. And the kids too. We're real glad to have you with us and just want to welcome you here and hope you enjoy your time with us.'

I pumped his hand again and asked him in.

'No,' he said. 'I'll let you settle in and have a taste of pie and then if you've got nothing fixed for tonight, why don't you come over for a barbecue?'

'Great,' I said. I fancied a big slab of Western beef especially from the next-door neighbours. And judging from the size of Martin, I didn't think he'd be likely to skimp on the portions.

He certainly didn't skimp, not one bit. And the friendliness was as warm and overwhelming as the treble T-bone steaks that came thudding down onto our plates, ringed by a mountain range of mashed potatoes. Out of the corner of my eye I saw their ten-year-old daughter with the same portion, so they weren't just testing me. Strangely, she wasn't yet as massive as Martin and Shirley who had to be carrying over forty stone between them. This made the two of them weigh about four of me; in fairness it was the three of them as Shirley was carrying their third child, which I was going to have to deliver a couple of months later. Still, they were checking me out and I wasn't going to appear a wimp, especially with my hair flowing down my back, so I whacked the dead steer and spuds down without a murmur. There in Rose Valley they were pleased that I could more than keep up with them; they were impressed, too, with the bloodiness of my steak, for in the West they like to char their meat to a crisp. 'I've seen cows hurt worse'n that, that recovered.' 'Shirley, bring a Band-Aid, I think we can save this steer.' So the checking-out was very gentle, very easy. There was no malice to these folks, no *side*. Bulky but straightforward.

Shirley and Martin were both teachers in the local school. Having a school and a hospital made Rose Valley more important than it seemed to deserve, but then a town of seven hundred people was pretty big in those parts of the Northern Prairies. Certainly big enough to merit six churches, which seemed excessive at first, but these folks had only come over sixty years before and were third-, second- and first-generation immigrants with their ethnic identities pretty much intact, and hard memories of survival in Ireland, Norway or the Ukraine in 1910 still vivid in their hearts. They *had been delivered* and still prayed fiercely in gratitude every Sunday, in their own churches in their own languages. Roman Catholics, Methodists, Anglicans, Ukrainian Orthodox, Baptist, Norwegian non-conformist. There were more churches than shops in Rose Valley, but then there is no more important commodity than God, something Nashville has known for a while. There was even a French Catholic chapel on the horizon in a hamlet called St Front that folks said was immortalized by Johnny Cash in a song from his wandering years before he became the President's best friend.

Though we were up in the Northern plains, this was still the mid-West and Country music was King. On that first night I heard there were several little country bands in the area and I'd have no trouble getting a gig. Later, when I got home, I switched back into Radio Des Moines, Iowa, and I didn't touch that dial again. The needle stayed there for the next four and a half months. I'd had my six months of C & W turnaround with Gram Parsons in London and here I was close to the source. Sure, we *were* way up North and there *were* more farmers than cowboys, but some raised cattle, many had horses, everyone listened to Country music and *everyone*, Indians and Immigrants alike, wore the real, pointed Texas boots.

As a fan and a victim of winkle-pickers in the past, I was eager to know how their feet were not being moulded into solid wedge shapes by the force of two hundred and fifty pounds of prime steer-fed

Ukrainian farmer bearing down into the boot day after day. I found out that the shape of the boot was like a cradle, with a high arch and a curve for the main body of the foot, a curve that would grow with age until some boots' toes pointed up to heaven like the caliph of Baghdad's. It wasn't until I got to San Francisco a year later, though, that I got my first pair of Tony Lamas. But that first night I had no real inkling of Indians, of the Prairie Population, of rape seed or of signing for your liquor in a back room at the chemist's. On my porch with a belly full of Bar-B-Q, with George Jones helplessly singing 'Not What I Had In Mind' from Des Moines. I saw the strength of the star light on a moonless night.

The jackpines over the way were black against the stars.

It looks like things are going to be OK.

Even the Teachers wear pointed boots.

☆ ★ ☆

It was called Rose Valley because roses never grew there and it was completely flat. The same principle as the Christmas Rose, which wasn't a rose and didn't bloom at Christmas, and was called *Helleborus niger* because the flower is white. It was once used for mental derangement, but whether to cause or cure is no longer certain.

The people of Saskatchewan had the same erratic sense of humour as the Christmas Rose. Very *country*, the same irony is in the best C & W songs. 'If You Don't Believe I Love You, Ask My Wife' matches the signs outside the little towns, sly smiles through the rape fields.

Outside Biggar,

NEW YORK
IS BIG BUT
THIS IS
BIGGAR
population still 700
Thanks

Thanks? Another good one was

TISDALE
LAND OF RAPE AND HONEY

I heard of Urine, Sask.

GREETINGS!
YOU'RE IN
URINE
pop. 400

People brought their own names over and were pretty pragmatic about it. Hendon was down the road from Rose Valley, south, on the way to the nearest doctor fifty miles away in Wadena. An old lady from just south of Mill Hill, London, came in 1910, called her home Hendon. A hundred and fifty people live there now but you still miss it if you blink, even in the Dial-a-Dat. And there's Rheinland, Sask. And little doubt about McTaggart, down the road from The Trossachs, Sask. I'd always been intrigued by the surrealism of Eyebrow, Sask., and, as a Hippie Doctor, saddened that I never got to Smoking Tent, Sask. Which was close to Hudson Bay, Sask., called that because it was nowhere near any lake at all, let alone Hudson's Bay. There you go again. A lot of Christmas Roses in Saskatchewan.

My favourite, call me an old romantic if you like, was always Love, Saskatchewan, on the way North, to the land of the Lakes, where the loons cry lonesome and the Northern Lights dance and hiss in the night sky.

WELCOME
YOU ARE NOW IN
LOVE
Gateway to the
Narrow Hills

The next morning was my first surgery and was the town's chance to check me out. I was still apprehensive and would be until my first medical emergency. Up till now I'd always had back-up. Sure, in the past I'd been given responsibility to act on my own decisions but there was always a senior registrar or a more experienced colleague around and all you'd get would be egg on your face for not knowing the answer. Here, *I was the only doctor for fifty miles* I kept saying to myself. Sure, again, I could pick up the blower and talk to the doc down the road, but when you think you're on a frontline, you imagine the worst. People being rushed in to the hospital with their guts hanging out, an arm torn from its socket in some appalling threshing accident or blood spurting six feet out of someone's neck and painting the wall of the casualty room. But this is the realm of paranoia and paranoia after all is *the fear of the unlikely.*

Whenever I've found a deep end I've always enjoyed the jump. It's just that the initial shock takes a little while to settle, and that first morning in the surgery I was shivering in my sneakers, waiting for the unlikely to happen. It did, but without the entrails on the carpet.

Mrs Yaholnitsky came in. She tottered bravely towards me.

'Achhh, Doktor, aieee, cchhere is the pain.'

She held on to the desk with one hand as she eased herself very slowly down into the chair. Her other arm crooked and her head eloquently bowed, she patted at the small of her back, wincing each time her hand hit the painful area.

'Cchhere, Doktor, oooff.'

She collapsed on to the chair and let out a great hiss like an old steam train stopping. The hiss went on and I thought she would deflate and shrink like a punctured balloon; but she kept up sharp intakes of breath each time she patted her bad back and stayed the same generous size. She was an old Ukrainian peasant who had come over when she was twenty and she was now well into her eighties. She had a scarf over her head and a black ground-length dress, a cross between *Fiddler on the Roof* and *The Cherry Orchard*. As I came round the desk to look at her back the movements became more frenetic, as if her hand were pecking at the pain, I started to feel round her lumbar region, pressing spots enquiringly through four layers of clothes.

'Yes, Doktor, cchhere, cchhere, yes.'

I mumbled and murmured reassuringly as I prodded around. As I seemed to be getting on the case, she suddenly leaned forward and grabbed her left knee with both gnarled hands and howled.

'And cchhere, Doktor, is match pain, very match.' The pain was plaiting her eyebrows but her beady old eyes watched my every move as I kneeled and felt her knee, pressing the sides thoughtfully and bending the knee gently from the ankle.

'Eeeecchh, haieee, Doktor, yes, is there, there.' I looked gratified but concerned at finding the source of the pain. 'Good, good,' I nodded sagely, soaking up her worry,' I think we can help a bit.'

At this Mrs Yaholnitsky started jabbing at her throat.

'This cchhere, Doktor, very bad pain, with lump cchhere, not swallow, is bad, very match pain.' She started to splutter and cough, almost retching, with one hand jabbing away and the other gripped tight round her throat as if she was strangling herself or trying to shift a potato which had stuck in her gullet. She was wheezing and gasping for breath, her face turning a nasty purple and her jugulars standing out like sausages running down her neck.

'Every night like this, Doktor, like big lump inside, cannot breathe, very hard, match pain, is very pain, aaiee.' Her head was rolling back and her eyes seemed to be slipping upwards. I felt her neck and was just about to point my torch down her throat when she started tapping her hip. And then her shoulder. And then her ankle, until she was touching herself all over, her hands racing about her body frantically pointing at different bits, each in greater agony than all the others put together. As it rose to a crescendo, an agonized Ukrainian ballet of pain with a thousand teeth that carried me up in its frenzy, I remembered a Russian phrase from my childhood.

'Mrs Yaholnitsky, *BOZHEMOI.*'

She stopped dead in her tracks and then spun round with the speed and grace of a figure skater.

'You spik Ukrainian, Doktor?'

She stared at me, her mouth agape in wonder, her body stilled, her eyes wide open and glazed with the sweet innocence that only a miracle can bring. She murmured as if she were intoning so many Hail Marys.

'Doktor spik Ukrainian. He spik Ukrainian, Ukrainian.'

'No, Mrs Yaholnitsky, I can only say My God! in Russian, *Bozhemoi.*'

With this she started to shake, her body fibrillating, her eyes staring, the mumbling chant moving into second gear. 'Ukrainian. Ukrainian, he spik Ukrainian.' I just stopped myself in time telling her I could also say *Ya Tibya Lyublyu*, Russian for I Love You. A quick sign of the cross and I'd have had my first disciple; I wasn't quite ready for the Second Coming, though, so I ushered her out and into Ruby's understanding arms.

'Tell her I don't speak Ukrainian, Ruby.'

'Why, that's wonderful, Doctor,' she said, a little hard of hearing. 'You're the first we've had who does.'

'No, no, I *don't* speak Ukrainian,' I whispered with a desperate hoarseness, 'I *don't*.' But I knew it was too late. The damage was done.

So I suppose I shouldn't have been too surprised that next morning at the surgery there was a line of nine elderly Ukrainian women all ready to pour out their troubles gratefully in their native tongue. They'd come in one by one glancing coyly as they walked across the room, sit down on the chair, their heads bowed in a kind of mental curtsey and put their hands together in the same precise way on their laps. Their eyes would rise slowly and adoringly, they'd take a deep breath and . . . whoosh! Quiet Flows the Don? You must be joking, these old girls rattled on and on as I waved my arms and tried to get a few words in edgeways. It took a lot of persuading to convince them that Mrs Yaholnitsky had got hold of the wrong end of the stethoscope, and I could tell that some of them didn't believe a word I said, and would speak in broken English only to indulge me.

It was my first inkling of how close-knit the community was, and how fast word got round. I was soon to find people would tell me what I'd said fifteen minutes before on the other side of town. And as time wore on and I felt more and more alone and longed at night for the touch of someone's flesh, for a body to wrap myself around, I knew there was no way I could mess around without the whole town knowing. At times I thought of Mary, long straight hair and almond eyes that smiled tantalizingly at me when I went shopping in the self-serve to where she was on the check-out, but she was stepping out with Wayne who worked in the butcher's shop next door. I didn't fancy a cleaver in my head with no other doctor around for fifty miles so I kept myself to myself. Being alone on the Prairies was all very Country and Western so I played and wrote songs night after night on the porch. Still in thrall of Gram, with the Flying Burrito Brothers on the record player and Des Moines on the radio, I moved away from the Sixties' singer-songwriter style I'd been in and plunged deeper into the heart and soul of Country music. I had already got drawn in by the fine irony of Country and was finding that the best way to deal with the self-indulgent pain of isolation was to laugh at it. And, of course, the best way to deal with the sexual frustration was masturbation, so I wanked myself silly those months out on the flatlands. I wanked so much I was surprised I had anything left between my legs when I left Rose Valley. Still, no one was hurt by it, no cleavers were thrown and as they say in the old joke, *you meet a better class of person that way.*

Indian
☆
Reservations

That Friday was the first time I met some of the Indians who lived on the reserve north-east of town near Little Nut Lake. East of the lake was Nut Mountain, so-called because no nuts grew there and it was completely flat. You get the picture by now.

The tribe was the Saulteaux, part of the Northern Woods Cree Indians. Like many of their brothers and sisters they were in a pretty sorry state and were patronized, feared or reviled by most of the white folks. I hadn't been out to the reserve yet but had seen some of them driving round town, seventeen at a time crammed into beaten up old '59 Chevvies, shock absorbers absorbed and the rear bumper trailing two inches above the ground.

Then on Friday there seemed to be a mysterious outbreak of infantile diarrhoea and vomiting. I was called to the casualty room of the little twenty-two-bed hospital and admitted two babies with identical symptoms for observation. No temperature, but both distressed and showing signs of gastro-intestinal upset. It all seemed straightforward until three more babies were brought in. I feared some kind of epidemic decimating the Indian population. Then my head nurse drew me aside.

'Don't worry about it, it's just the tobacco they use.'

I didn't understand.

'Every time the parents want to go away for the weekend,' she explained, 'they stuff tobacco in their mouths and up their bottoms. It gives them vomiting and diarrhoea. We still have to admit the kids for

25

observation even though we know what's been done and that the kids will be fine in the morning.'

I was horrified and, full of righteous indignation, railed and shouted at the next parents who brought their retching babies in. I was a Real White Man, and decided we couldn't have the hospital taken advantage of in this way. I fumed and boiled as we admitted eleven children that evening. All the parents were doing was going down the road to party all weekend with friends in another tribe, using the hospital facilities as a kind of crèche. They knew we would keep the kids in till Monday when they'd come back to collect them on the way home. I was outraged and decided, like the callow young officer straight out of military academy and posted to command a platoon of battle-hardened veterans at the front, to do things by the book. I wasn't going to have valuable hospital beds used up just so a bunch of Indians could go off and get drunk. In an hour I had absorbed the whole atavistic white suspicion and contempt of the Indians.

As Willie Nelson sang on the radio from Des Moines that night, though, 'Time Changes Everything', and it's funny how your perception of things can turn around suddenly and completely.

It took a while to see the real story. I thought that the jackpines across the road, round the house, had been planted, that the Prairie had always been treeless. Then, like the drawing where, depending how you look at it, the two faces become the vase, I saw that the jackpines had always been there and the rest of the trees had just been ripped out.

It was the same with the Indian kids coming in shitting every Friday. At first I was the White Man, an aggressive Medical Redneck. I don't know, you try to help these people and what do they do? They just want to get drunk with their friends . . . and yet . . .

It wasn't an attitude I could maintain for very long. Something kept niggling away; a lot of doctors may be frustrated policemen but I've never felt too comfortable wagging my finger. Not one of the world's great castigators, I've never been much good at telling people off. But I was still outraged, pompous and ignorantly indignant about the Indians dumping their kids on the hospital when I first saw one of the young Indian guys sniffing gasoline. At that moment the Friday Kids slipped into a new perspective.

Jim Wounded Eagle was the town gas-sniffer. He was only just seventeen but already had one foot and a nose in the grave. He was the only sniffer in Rose Valley but there was a tribe thirty miles down the road where whole families were doing it. The first time I saw Jim he was standing in the middle of the road, legs splayed apart to steady himself against the buffeting winds of desolation, a man alone in the wilderness. He turned his head and pointed his face at me, but his eyes were glazed over, soft and empty as jelly. I looked into them and saw no brain behind. He was gone. Out in the middle of the Prairie, without booze or heroin or sleepers, he had managed to find the end of the line, as terminal as the worst junkie or alcoholic.

It's not too hard. You've just got to want to get there, to the big wipe-out. Wrench off that filler cap, get your face into the pipe and snort. I'd see Jim hunched over the back of an old Pontiac, hanging on to the fins, his nose stuck in the gas pipe, heaving and wheezing as he melted his mind down for the day. Although I'd seen people as blocked out and as spiritually dead on Ladbroke Grove or 42nd Street or the grim dust-covered Victorian ward of a long-stay mental hospital in the long-stay suburbs of London, Jim Wounded Eagle's buckled knees and sightless stare shocked me rigid. I didn't *expect* it. Not because he was the Noble Savage being corrupted by the white man's ways. Nothing like that. I just didn't expect *that* degree of pain or *that* fierce an anaesthetic. And if the pain, the humiliation of being a second-class citizen in his own country, treated like a sponger with fear and condescension by the white folks, hanging on to a life empty of respect, if it was all too much then it wasn't surprising he chose to blot it out. And it put a different perspective on the kids stuffed full of tobacco every Friday. Now I could see what to do. The two faces had turned into a vase.

I knew we'd need to look after the children anyway, it's just we didn't need the excuses. Nor did the kids. So I put the word out just to bring the kids in without shoving tobacco down their throats or up their arses, we'd look after them anyway. A few sick ones came in that weekend but they were all happy and smiling a week later. No baccy, no shits. A hospital full of cheerful little Saulteaux children, running around laughing with the nurses or with an old woman lying in bed suffering from a severe kidney infection. Much better, and closer to my dream of a hospital full of *healthy* people.

Meanwhile, outside, Jim Wounded Eagle was still howling without hearing, his poor wobbly rubber legs bouncing him from wall to wall, carrying him somehow to the next gas tank. It could have been the gas tank of his dreams if only he had any.

☆ ★ ☆

As the days and weeks wore on I realized there wasn't ever going to be a second-rate sunset, that each night colours would rage and slash across the sky, crimsons, blood reds, oranges and golds, and each night it would resolve with idyllic pale blues and deep, quiet purples, a vision of peace and eternal calm. Very still. Just what the Hippie Doctor ordered. And then the cloak of night and all that stuff.

Then someone told me about Ma Jensen's Hill. It was just a rise in the road, really, but it went up to thirty feet or thereabouts, and those thirty feet raised you out of the flat sea of rape and corn for a grandstand view of God's Great Lightshow. With those thirty feet, on Ma Jensen's Hill, you were on the floor of the Sky but the top of the World.

Those thirty feet were worth every inch of the seventeen-mile drive from Rose Valley. A thirty-four-mile round trip. Nothing. Regularly I'd call the doc in Wadena to take any desperate calls, jump into Dial-a-Dat and head for Ma Jensen's for a quick dose of Oneness With It All. Up on the Hill, I'd spray myself all over with OFF! and settle down to watch the sinking sun through a frenzied fog of mosquitoes. Frenzied and frustrated because behind the hideous repellent they could smell me. *They knew I was in there*, that I was worth waiting for and that eventually the OFF! would evaporate. They started about two feet away, a pale and flimsy cloud, and gradually moved in, the veil coalescing, thickening, the buzzing getting louder and more excited, the blood-lust boiling. So as the sun was dipping down below the grain elevators on the horizon the skeeters would be just six inches away from my flesh. I'd go back to the car beating a rearguard action with the OFF! as I opened the door so as not to take any of the bastards back to Rose Valley with me. They had a murderous bite, more like flying lobsters than mosquitoes. But they couldn't spoil the sunsets, and even the World's Smallest Hire Car would be purring as I slid back to town. It almost felt that I had smoked an enormous spliff.

Which of course I hadn't, being the caring human being and responsible physician that I am.

Do Loons
☆
see the Lights?

Over the first couple of months in
Rose Valley, I had got to know the doctors in the group medical practice
in Wadena on the few times I'd popped down the road – just forty miles
– for a cup of tea and a chat. On the grid roads slicing straight as a die
across the green and golden flatness, forty miles was a blink of an eye.
Even in the mingy Dial-a-Dat, distances and space became so accessible
you could pop them in your pocket. It was a measure of my loneliness
that I'd go that far to be sociable with a doc and his family; being a bit of
a medicophobe I'd normally drive forty miles to get *away* from a group
practice.

In the early Seventies, when British GPs were really poorly paid,
many young docs came out to Canada to make lots of money for a few
years, then go back home to buy themselves into a good practice. It was
OK for the docs themselves, who just worked hard all the time, but
difficult for the wives who must have been bored shitless. They could
hardly have affairs in such small communities. Unless that's what
Group Practice means. If they weren't cooking, watching TV or making
more loose covers for the lounge suite, the local paper was all they had
to read. Now the *Wadena News* was so parochial that it made the *North
London Press* look like the *New York Times*. Having folks over to tea was
big news and I was a bit surprised that I never had any of my tea breaks
reported. Family visits were front page headlines:

THOMPSONS COME TO TEA

Last week Alan and Dottie Waszynski of Hendon, Sask.,
played host to family they hadn't seen for three years.
Alan's sister Amy was delighted to visit her brother and
sister-in-law for the first time since she married John
Thompson and moved to his home town of Killarney,
Ontario. John and Amy were on their way to Vancouver
to visit John's parents who retired there after John's
father John was pensioned off after breaking his leg
badly in a pit disaster where three of his workmates were
tragically killed after an underground explosion caused a
serious cave-in that tragically killed them though he was
lucky to escape almost intact.

Scones

The tea was delicious and it was a big treat for all when
Dottie produced drop scones, a favourite for Alan and
Amy when Ma Waszynski used to make them for them
when they were children at home in Hendon. There
were cakes, too, of course, for Amy had brought a big
fruit cake and Dottie had made a lovely three-layer jam
and chocolate sponge cake.

Twins

Alan's sister Amy was the proud mum when she
showed off her ten-month-old twins Ruth and Ellie.
They are in the best of health and pretty as two pictures
and are looking forward to seeing their grannie and
grandad, even though his leg was broken in a mining
accident, for the first time. The Thompsons stayed all of
Thursday afternoon before they had to leave, replete
with food. All good things must come to an end, so they
say, so they all said their tearful goodbyes.

So I got to know them over tea and on the telephone when I'd call up to
check how to deal with a splinter of steel stuck in someone's eye or a
barbed fish hook buried in a young angler's neck. One of the guys even
came up to anaesthetize someone for me to remove their appendix.
Sounds like chickenfeed but normally we'd send an appendix case to
Saskatoon, for if anything went wrong in the middle of an operation, the
immediate back-up was not so easy to come by. While the classic
appendicectomy is a simple and, in its own way, elegant operation,
appendicitis can be mimicked by many other conditions; whole books
are devoted to its differential diagnosis. The vestigial worm, hanging
like an afterthought off the beginning of the large intestine, can lie
almost anywhere in the abdominal cavity and can be confused with
anything from an ovarian cyst to gall-bladder trouble. So no one should
be cavalier with its removal. The case we took on was a young man of
twenty whose symptoms were so acute and so severe there was a real
danger of perforation with the threat of a nasty dose of peritonitis. My

colleague was anaesthetizing the lad within thirty-five minutes of my phone call and I was closing him up with the neatest of subcutaneous stitches within the hour. In fact, as happens in fifty per cent of appendicectomies, however acute the symptoms, I had removed a completely normal appendix and found no cause for his pains. He recovered pretty uneventfully. Funny thing, life.

After a while I managed to get one of the Wadena doctors to stand in for me so I could go north to get my head together, as they say in San Francisco. I borrowed a tent and headed up the grid road through Tisdale, Land of Rape and Honey, through Love, Gateway to the Narrow Hills, and through Nipawin Provincial Park up to Little Bear Lake, where for the first time in months there were no people and no phone. Up there in Northern Canada it's all woods and water, lots of lakes, rivers and forests. Very alone but not too quiet because of the calling of the loons. Coming through the silver mists hanging over the lakes, the loon's cry is heart-wrenchingly desolate and can reduce grown men to tears. I certainly got a lump in my throat many times hearing the pathetic sobbing through the trees, echoing plaintively across the empty lakes, a cry of unrequited love.

For that's what it was; an Indian princess and a young brave fell in love but were from different, warring tribes, or he was from the wrong side of the Lake, something like that. Some kind of Woods Cree version of Romeo and Juliet, anyway, and they were forbidden to marry. He was turned into a bird, as so often happens, and as he flew off to his lonesome exile he tugged at her heart with his mournful cry. Unable to bear him leaving with no memory of her, the princess tossed her bracelet to him as he passed. It fell over his head and gave the loon the black necklace it has round the base of its slender grey neck.

So for two days and nights all I heard was the sighing of the wind and the loons, until on the second night as I was curling up inside my tent everything suddenly stopped. I lay there listening, waiting for a call to cut through the thickness of the silence, waiting for a breath of wind to break the eerie stillness, but nothing happened. Nothing, that is, until I became aware of a strange *swishing* sound like long, sweet grass being softly scythed or the rustling of taffeta. It was a bit too other-worldly to check out, but however deep I curled into my sleeping-bag, it wouldn't go away. So gingerly I crawled to the end of the tent, unzipped the doorflap and stuck my head out.

I was poleaxed, felled to the ground and rolled over. Though I felt no pain I thought I had been hit over the head leaving me lying there on my back with just my head sticking out of the tent flap. That must have been why I was seeing stars like they do in comics just before the egg-shaped lump sprouts on top of the head. But I felt my head and felt no lump and I blinked a few times and the lights were still there.

The whole sky, from one sweet star-filled side to another, was filled with a pulsating glow which retracted and shot out like the limbs of a gigantic amoeba. As a limb shot out into a still-dark starry patch on the horizon I would hear that inter-stellar swishing and the edges of the offshoot would hang and drip down the sky like a crystal-bead curtain in the most delicate of pale pastel pinks and greens. The lights were seeping down and soaking into the dark parchment of the night sky. As I watched them shimmering and scintillating like sequins and rhinestones thrown on to a moonlit waterfall, I knew that I was watching the Aurora Borealis, the Northern Lights. I couldn't move to save my life and stayed lying there with my head still sticking out of the tent. I tried once but as soon as I got to my feet the Lights burst out even brighter and danced an even wilder tarantella across the sky which just flattened me again. As I lay there I wondered what in hell the Indians would have made of them. I was a fully qualified twentieth-century techno-atheist and *I* knew that God was smiting me. It wasn't till I met Hank that I found out it was the sparks flying from medicine men battling in the sky, on the edges of the Other World.

When I got back to Rose Valley I blathered on like a kid who's fallen in the ice-cream, 'Did you see?? . . . Did you see? . . . Did you see them, the Lights, they were UNBELIEVABLE, they were . . . they were . . .'

'Yeah, yeah, Doc, the Lights were out last night. They were fine.'

☆ ★ ☆

Joni Mitchell comes from Prince Albert, Sask., and everyone in Saskatchewan knows her and has met at least one member of her family. It was impossible to go to any barbecue, rodeo, Norwegian or Ukrainian wedding without being asked to dance – 'Hi, you're the new doctor in Rose Valley, huh? Like to dance?' – and it seemed impossible to dance without being asked if I knew Joni Mitchell. It can't have been the medical degree – 'Well, Doc, you know about Joni Mitchell's colitis? Have you talked to her about it? Told her about high fibre foods yet?' – no, it was much more likely the hair.

'So you're the new doctor in Rose Valley? You going to stay past the summer?'

'Well, probably not much beyond autumn, I've got to do a bit more travelling.'

'Pardon me though, nothing personal, but you look more like a Hippie than a doctor. You dance fine, though.'

'Thanks. So do you.'

'Do you know Joni Mitchell? She's from Prince Albert across the way a bit and I'm a friend of her Uncle Jim's. I was dancing with him at a wedding last month. He's a real fine dancer.'

'Well, I don't know her very personally but two years ago I played guitar with her in a field on a Spanish island a couple of times. I jammed with her if you know what I mean.'

But then that, as the Colonel would say, is Volume II.

King Bighead

The most aggressive man I met in Rose Valley was called King Bighead. Not *because* he was aggressive, it just happened to be his name. He was squat, thick-set and seemed to particularly resent women, although at a pinch he'd beat up men too. He was a right bastard and his name was made in heaven along with Thomas Crapper's, the famous sanitary engineer. He'd be released from jail, get drunk and go back to Nut Lake Reserve, beat up a mate or two, get picked up by the Mounties and be thrown back into pokey all within the space of six hours. If he couldn't find a mate to smash, he'd go and break a girlfriend's arm. I had to set two women's arms, one of them twice, after the King had had a go, so I wasn't his biggest fan. He'd been doing it for years according to my head nurse, and he wasn't about to stop. He just *loved* to break those women's arms, and no amount of jail or cutting off his booze would change his mind. It was as if he had to live up to his name.

One night I was in the middle of a very steamy dream, on the symbolic side of things but still reasonably erotic. Out on the Prairies I took what I got and was grateful . . .

I was jolted into semi-consciousness by the telephone ringing by my bed. I reached over, switched the light on, screwed my eyes up to see it was four in the morning and grabbed the phone.

'Dr Hutt? The hospital here. The Mounties just called to say they're bringing two Indians in. There's been a pickaxe fight or something.'

Pickaxe fight? Where am I? What the hell's going on? I pulled my trousers on, stuck my feet in my shoes and grabbed the clock again to make sure it really was four o'clock. Blimey. Pickaxe fight. *What is all this?* I was surfacing fast now, hitting reality but still not knowing quite

34

what kind of dream I was in. I got to the casualty room in my shirt-tails just before the cops brought the stretcher in. One of the Indians was flat out, moaning and cursing, while the other was walked in and helped down on to a chair.

I went over to the bed and realized it was none other than ... King Bighead, holding his head in his hands, wailing low.

'Jesus Chrice, Jeeeeezuss Chrice.'

His face, his hands and the front of his shirt and vest were all covered in blood. As I tried to move his hands away to get a better look he moaned louder and struggled weakly.

'Jeee-zuss ... Jeeeee-zusss Chrice ...' He was very drunk and running on automatic. One of the cops held up a bloodied pickaxe that looked like it could have laid half the Canadian Pacific Railway.

'This is what done it, doc.'

Jesus, I thought to myself, this old boy had better see a doctor quick ... but ... oh, shit! that's me. And this is the emergency I've been dreading. Uh, oh, the pick stops here. The blood started to drain from my face as more blood trickled through Bighead's fingers. I took a grip on myself, stiffened my upper lip and gingerly prised his fingers apart. Blood was seeping slowly from a wound in the centre of his forehead. He didn't struggle as the nurse and a cop held his arms by his side and I peeled apart two flaps of skin.

'Jeeezuss Chrice.' I could have said that myself as I looked into the wound. His mate had driven the pickaxe right between his eyes and, as I mopped the blood and moved the skin flaps aside, I found myself looking an inch and a half into the King's frontal lobes. There was his brain tissue, soft and vulnerable, looking back at me. Were I not a doctor, I'd wonder that Bighead could be alive, but I'd heard of famous cases with jack-hammers that had shot back a bolt which smashed through the forehead, cutting off the frontal lobe but not killing the victim. A layman's lobotomy.

So it was dramatic but simple. I stopped most of the bleeding by applying pressure and coagulated a couple of stubborn bleeders with diathermy forceps, a pair of electric tweezers which burn and close open vessels. No problem and no pain for the King. I knew he'd survive the two-hour journey to the neurosurgery department in Saskatoon so I sent him off with the Mounties, went home and crawled back into bed.

A week later he was back with a smile on his face and a bandage round his head. In fact the smile rarely left his face from then on. He was, as they say, a changed man. His friend's pickaxe had done what so many American neurosurgeons did back in the Twenties and Thirties when, under financial pressure to clear the crowded mental hospitals of the time, they performed thousands of lobotomies to send out happy vegetables into the community where they would trouble no one and not be a drain on the state psychiatric facilities. I'm certainly not advocating lobotomy here but King Bighead did do a lot of smiling from then on. And he never broke a woman's arm again.

I love the fierce pride of people who live in places everyone else derides. The run-down inner-city areas of places like Glasgow or Liverpool or the East End of London all traditionally had a tight-knit self-sufficiency about them. It was the same with Saskatchewan, a place no one went to live, a place to cross on the way west, lying between even more prairies in Manitoba and Alberta, in the middle of an endless drive, straining to see the first jagged outline of the Rockies in the distance. A terrible place to travel across but an inspiring place to stop in to search the sky. The least popular state for other Canadians, Saskatchewan was lower on the scale than Newfoundland or the North-West Territories. In the face of all this, the people who lived there made 1971 Saskatchewan Homecoming Year, to get all those who had left the place to come back and visit family and friends and, who knows?, perhaps even to stay. It sounded like a desperate move, but was an indication of the pride of the folks on the Prairies. If people like the doc who briefed me in London sneered at the unrelenting flatness, they would say:

'Well, there ain't no mountains round to spoil the Prairies' view,' and leave it at that. They knew for themselves how beautiful that prairie view could be, how it could change before their eyes, but they weren't going to let *any* turkey know that.

In the Thirties, the Dust Bowl ravaged much of the mid-West, and Saskatchewan didn't escape lightly. The southern part of the state dried up and they called it the Dirty Thirties. There they would say:

'Hell, ain't no *trees* around to spoil the Prairies' view.' I remember the same laconic sense of humour as a kid in Glasgow and knew I could get on well with these folks.

Lying Prostate

Doctors often diagnose illnesses differently. It's fairly traditional. Sometimes they favour a particular diagnosis for a certain group of people; an obvious example is hysteria, uniquely applied to women. After all, whoever heard of a hysterical man? It's a medical impossibility. But what does hysterical mean? Usually that the doctor simply doesn't like the woman, that he (though, surprisingly, it can be she) *can't get on with her.*

Sometimes different countries or cultures favour diagnoses that others deny. Until recently, cellulite was a complaint of French women only, scoffed at by English medical men. ('Well, it's not really *medical*, is it, just *women* bothered about their thighs, just vanity really.') How then did English women start to get cellulite? For they surely have it now, or at least *it is diagnosed.* Did they catch it when we joined the Common Market? I expect so.

Diagnosis is often a way of denying other possibilities

One illness I especially cherished was chronic prostatitis, commonly diagnosed throughout the North American continent but only rarely encountered in England. Englishmen just didn't get it and certainly did not have the massage treatment so liberally handed out in the Colonies. Prostatitis is a long-standing inflammation, probably following infection, deep in the substance of the prostate (usually mispronounced the *prostrate*) gland. The prostate is a chestnut-sized lump which produces semen and lies at the root of the genitals. It can be felt through the front wall of the rectum, about two inches up inside the rectum. It is said to be pleasurable and exciting for some to have the prostate stroked. I wouldn't know myself, as I don't really enjoy things being stuck up my behind, trapped as I always have been in the twilight world of the heterosexual.

My first surgical job was in Urology and Proctology which is exactly where you'd expect to find chronic prostatitis. But in six months of working *down below*, in six months of euphemisms – 'How's the water-works? And the motions?', which gave new meaning to the idea of going through the motions – I didn't do a single prostatic massage. Even the suggestion of making the diagnosis was almost to blacken a man's good name. There was the feeling, too, of something namby-pamby about it, not anything a Real Man would get. If there was some kind of clear discharge which showed no obvious infecting organisms, then it was simply *an excess of semen*, something an Englishman often produces.

Out on the Prairies, though, I was doing several prostatic massages every week. The good Dr Datta had many farmers and cowboys with clogged-up prostates on his books.

Regularly these big guys would come in for me to massage their little chestnuts better. And these guys were *BIG*; my neighbour Martin was no exception. They worked hard and ate hard, and were built like brick shithouses. They'd get up on to the couch a little sheepishly, pull their jeans down, and curl up in a foetal position facing the wall with their cowboy boots still on. Then, crouched over with my arm straight out and my finger stuck up inside some two-hundred-and-eighty-pound Ukrainian farmer's arse stroking away at his prostate, Time Would Stand Still.

One of those holy moments when we wonder, once again, at the Meaning of it All.

The meaning of what all? Hutt, what in hell are you going on about? We don't need to listen to your depraved ramblings, and if we don't need it then the folks who buy this book sure don't. They want to hear about Hank, that's what they paid their money for.

Well, I'm sorry, Colonel Frank, but I wanted to give them a bit of background.

BACKGROUND??? Look, boy, the money we're paying you we want a good big hunk of *Foreground*. Forget the back-ground, let's have a bit of Hank.

But, Colonel, the folks like the idea I'm a doctor, it makes them . . .

Listen, screw the doctoring. Who needs to finish up somebody's asshole? Remember Hank's audience, eight to eighty. *Extended Demographics*, right? This could be a Family Book. Get on the case before we take you off it, OK?

OK, Colonel, OK.

It was odd, but Hank and I never met for a long time though our paths kept criss-crossing through the early Seventies.

Look, we told you to give us Hank and you go back to what *you* **were doing.**

I'm sorry Colonel, I thought it . . .

Don't *think***, man, WRITE.**

If you say so Colonel. Maybe it'll be easier if I put both of us
in the third person?

**Do what you like as long as you don't put us all up some
goddam Russki farmer's asshole again. Keep it clean, for
Chrissake, keep it clean.**

Calgary Stampede

As it happened, Hank had passed through Saskatchewan a year before Sam got there. He had come up through Minnesota on the Norwegian route, from Sheboygan Falls, Wisconsin where he had foundered on the rocks of a rancorous marriage for two years. He had left his native Wangford on the northern Suffolk stretches of the A12 in the mid-Sixties to search for his father . . .

> **That's volume II, Hutt, that's volume II. This starts in '71, all right?**
> Sorry.

There was an uncanny parallel, too, for while he was in Sheboygan Hank, who was then just plain old Henry Hardman, did a home-study veterinary course. He didn't pass, of course. He was too busy having an unhappy marriage and dreaming of Country music, dreams his wife didn't share, scornful of what she called 'Apple-Pie Music'. But he learned enough basics in the vet course to pass as a doctor and on his travels he did occasional locums here and there, to keep himself going on the road. They were mostly quick weekend gigs, but once he fooled a whole Prairie town for three weeks before they found out that he wasn't even a horse doctor. No harm had been done, he'd cured quite a few, so they thanked him and let him go. They even gave him a big Kuubasa, Ukrainian garlic sausage, and a pack of Lefsa, thin Norwegian potato pancakes, to make multi-cultural sandwiches so that he wouldn't go hungry on his travels.

All the time, Hank was driven to head West, into the sun, turning his back on the tragedies of his past. He knew but wouldn't admit to himself that the chance of finding his father was minimal and that perhaps he was really searching for *himself* instead. Heavy on his heart were his two failed marriages, one in Wangford and the last in Wisconsin. Little did he know that on the road ahead were a few more marriages, and many more heartaches. He was what they used to call a marrying fool. His mother, an American truck driver posted to Suffolk during the War, had married Henry Hardman Snr and settled down near Wangford, making his father one of the few GI *bridegrooms* of the time. A woman of strict moral upbringing, she had always said to young Henry 'Have as many affairs as you like, son, but make them all legal.' And like all good boys, he didn't want to disappoint his mother.

Look, we told you about volume II.
Yes, I know, Colonel, but the folks have to know what makes Hank tick.
OK, OK, as long as you don't give away too much. Just remember the folks have only paid for *Vol III*.
All right, Colonel, I'll bear that in mind.

By the time he hit Calgary, Alberta, young Henry was full of remorse about leaving his second wife. Deep down inside he blamed his mother for pushing him into hasty marriages, but that thought was intolerable and he couldn't admit it to himself. Otherwise he was spiritually wide open, vulnerable but not defensive, ready for anything. In this mental state, he met his first Hippie friends in Calgary and had his first serious drug experiences.

His first acid trip was indeed a deeply serious experience. His new friends called themselves Buddhists and started by showing Henry the peace of meditation, and getting him to study Timothy Leary and Richard Alpert's book *The Psychedelic Experience*. This was based on *The Tibetan Book of the Dead*, a classic book used to take a dying person through the *Bardos*, the different stages of spiritual enlightenment possible during the death experience. Not that Henry was going to die, but that he would experience ego-loss, the disappearance of his wordly attachment to his idea of *Himself*. The Calgary Buddhists felt that the acid trip, a Rocketship to God, was not a valid experience without proper spiritual preparation. Otherwise, at best, it could only be a synthetic ecstasy, a Calgary Stampede, a cheap ticket into a kaleidoscopic palace of fun. And as any doctor will tell you, too much fun isn't good for you.

It wasn't just the preparation either, for Henry's first trip was properly devotional. They fasted the day before. On the way up into Innerspace, before the boosters fell away, pushing through the clouds of attachment, buffeted by the winds of fearful anticipation as they were visited by the Good Demons and the Bad Demons, they even listened to a recording of Krishnamurti giving one of his talks in his tiny birdlike voice:

'What is Love? What is Desire?'

'Without desire there is no pain.'

And without payin' there is no book. Cut the gook horseshit and get on with it.

Hang on, Colonel, we're nearly there. Give me five more minutes.

OK, five, but that's all.

So Henry got his first glimpse of the Great Beyond, of that Radiant Shore, and was bowled over. But Calgary always was a bit of a spiritual wasteland and re-entry was a little more difficult than he expected. Over the next few days he found himself becoming more and more disillusioned with his new friends. In the aftermath of the acid he found himself less able to compromise. So many doors had been flung open, he was having to find new ways of dealing with the world. If he was vulnerable before he was naked now. But the Hardmans were well named and day by day, Henry grew stronger. He felt an inner core of resilience develop like a spiritual backbone, as if his soul was sitting up straight with its eyes wide open.

But his Buddhist buddies were getting too pious for their own good, and Henry felt he could see right through them. They all seemed to be self-congratulatory about their meditative successes. They were almost competitively blissing out, seeing who could get deeper in touch with the non-self beyond, and who could be *completely* without Ego. Are they crazy? thought Henry. Didn't they see what I saw? Doesn't their reading Krishnamurti, their studying Gurdgieff, their meditation show them *anything*? It seemed so obvious to him, that they were all so *attached* to their achievements in just the way all their teachers were warning them against. They were using things like the I Ching and Tarot as toys, becoming more and more the people they were trying not to be.

They were Hippie Fundamentalists who hadn't entirely grasped the fundamentals.

Henry couldn't cope with the severity of their Macrobiotic Diet Number 7, basically brown rice and brown rice. And water. These guys thought that if a fast was good for ten days, it'd be dynamite for ten months, so they were wasting away, getting boils, bleeding gums and cracked lips and saying how groovy it was, the poison was all coming out. In his defence Georges Ohsawa, the father of Macrobiotics, would say that he only intended Number 7 as a ten-day job and it was just

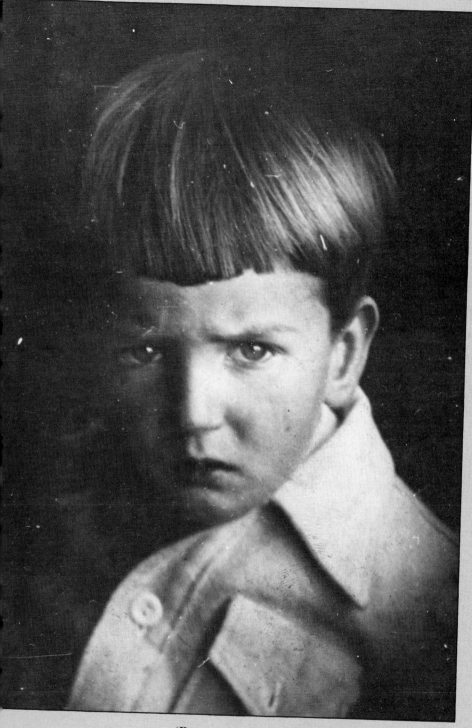

'Poor wee lad.'
Here's Hank in pain already, fifteen years before his first marriage.

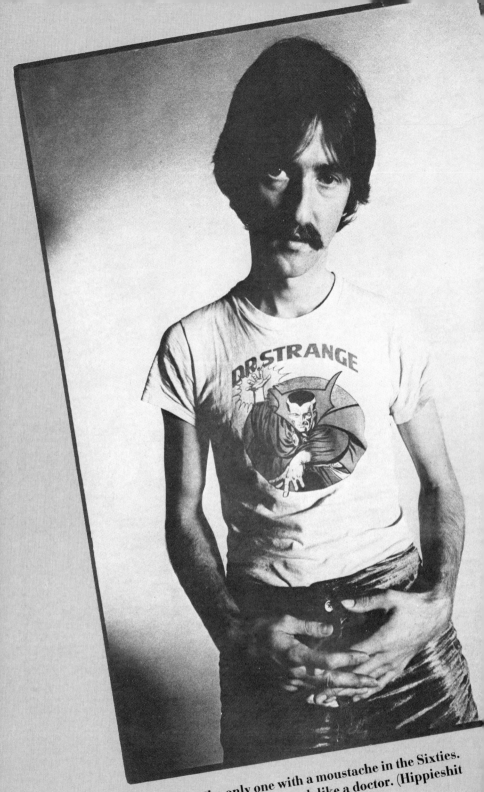

Hank wasn't the only one with a moustache in the Sixties.
Here I am trying my best to look like a doctor. (Hippieshit
fans will notice the crushed velvet trousers.)

Hank fooling himself that he really *is* a singing gynaecologist.

The realisation slowly dawns on Hank that the cowboy boot implant to the left side of his neck wasn't one of his best ideas. The operation was a success, but the boot died.

'I can look like Hank, I can wear Hank's suit, I can even
play his guitar, but in my heart I know I'm just a
gatecrasher in the atrium of pain.'

crazy Westerners who misread his instructions. But Ohsawa was a man of strong ironic sensibility who must have been laughing up his kimono more than once.

In Calgary, Henry read Ohsawa's book *You Are All Sanpaku* in which he argues that if you can see the whites of your eyes *underneath your iris it is a sign of deep mental and spiritual disquiet.* Things must be adjusted in your life so that the iris can sink blissfully on to the pacific horizon of the lower eyelid. Henry saw a smidgeon of irony there but was further disillusioned to see his Hippie pals checking their Sanpaku status in the mirror every morning and evening, and even cheating their whites away by tilting their heads backwards.

Henry was getting itchy feet.

Years later, he heard belatedly of Ohsawa's death. Some say he died of a heart attack but Hank preferred to believe the story that he died from an overdose of Japanese strawberries. All foods should be balanced, Ohsawa said, integrating yin and yang, the two opposites of existence. Some foods were yin and some yang. Colour, taste, sweetness, shape, all these factors went to make a food more one than the other.

Japanese strawberries are very yin, so by eating a gallon of them in one go as was rumoured, Ohsawa *yinned himself out* and committed Macrobiotic Hara-kiri.

Henry knew that he had just been put in touch with a lot of fundamental truth but also that his understanding of that truth was being eroded the longer he stayed in Calgary. The Buddhists were sadly as full of cant and hypocrisy as the society they were rejecting. They kept saying they wanted to go to the mountains to get their heads together as they rolled another joint and stared at the ceiling. Henry couldn't stand it any longer. He would pace up and down through the house, go to the window, open it and look out and point at the Rockies as if the Buddhists hadn't seen them rising out of the plains only eighty miles away.

'Look, they're just over there, you can see them from this window,' he'd say impatiently. 'All you have to do is stand on the street corner, stick your thumb out and you could be there before tea time.'

Which is exactly what Henry did because no one took a blind bit of notice.

Is that it? No more Hippieshit?

No, Colonel Frank, that's it. Thank you for your patience.

Have a nice day.

Hank is a man without Ego. He lost it as Henry in 1971 and has never been able to find it since.

There Goes
☆
my Everything

During the month before I left London for the Prairies I'd been stepping out with Shirley Donaldson, a tall, slender Californian who had left San Francisco to travel round Europe since her marriage broke up a year and a half before. We had quite an intense farewell and resolved that when I was near the end of my time in Saskatchewan, she would come out west in her VW bus, pick me up and we would drive off into the sunset and live happily ever after. We kind of knew we were fooling ourselves but it was a nice deception, and we hadn't had time to fall out of lust. It had been like a holiday romance.

I thought about her out there under the Great Sky, and for a while we exchanged a few letters. After I'd been there for nearly four months, I got one out of the blue to say she was on her way out West after all and she'd be passing through Rose Valley. Although in my heart I knew there wasn't much of a future for us, after months of lonely days and nights on the Prairies it was easy enough to rekindle the flames of fantasy. From then on I couldn't wait for Shirley to arrive in her microbus and carry us off to a Pacific paradise. Sitting on my three-piece suite in Dr Datta's brown-toned bungalow, I had waking dreams as purple as my steamy sleeping ones. The thought of Shirley's long legs snaking around me once more kept me going through the last dark days of my stay in Rose Valley. By now I was keen to get on the road.

I was ready to beat feet.

Two weeks after the letter, Shirley turned up.

With Eric.

She had met Eric while I was out in Canada, and though underneath it all I was secretly relieved, I retreated to the solace of Country music. I stuck my hands in the dishwater and turned up the George and Tammy. OK, it was self-indulgent. So what? If I was fooling myself, that's often how rejection is. There's a lot of self-inflicted pain about in life and Country music is there to laugh at it.

'If today was a fish I'd throw it back in' was pretty much how I felt when Shirley and Eric turned up together, but we all got on fine. When they left for the Promised Land two days later, Eric gave me his backpack so that I could get out on the road and hitch.

Well, mate, I thought as I waved them goodbye, he gets the girl and the truck and I get a rucksack full of broken promises and shattered dreams. Ha, ha. Ain't life cruel? But I smiled to myself for in my heart, somehow, I knew it was a blessing in disguise.

In the Blue
☆
Canadian Rockies

In the Blue Canadian Rockies
Spring is sighing through the trees,
And the golden poppies are blooming
By the banks of Lake Louise.

Lake Louise stretched out before him a milky, pale-turquoise moonstone millpond, cradled in the arms of the mountains on either side, its head nestled in the pillows of the seven glaciers whose waters fed it and made it glow. He'd heard about the colour before and it did have an unearthly, almost Disney glow about it. A thick colour, a colour from within. They said this luminous quality came from the glacial silt but looking out over the still waters with their encircling mountains, Henry could tell it was the light of a million opals, crushed in the hands of a black-eyed Princess who lived at the top of the Seven Glaciers, straddling the jagged peaks of the Great Divide. The Pacific was over on her left side, the great plains on her right. And at her feet, lying there with its tranquil blue fire, rested Lake Louise. The Princess would crush opals and toss them on to the ice of the glaciers so that they would shimmer and spangle in the moonlight. She loved this and thought it looked like the glaciers laughing with the moon. But when any clouds came over and hid the moon's smile, she would feel sad and cry and her warm tears would wash all the opal dust into Lake Louise.

> *And the golden poppies are blooming*
> *By the banks of Lake Louise.*

Henry sang low to himself even though it was a late summer evening and the golden poppies had bloomed and gone. He felt he'd come to the end of a great journey or at least an important staging post. The song had been one of his favourites for a long time and the beauty of the place, for once, matched his dreams. A very rare thing. There was room, too, for his mind to wander and to wonder. He had felt frustrated and shackled in Calgary for the last two weeks with his Buddhist buddies who seemed to be blind to everything around them on their compulsive journey within. They had forgotten that the knowledge from that journey was also to help them on their great voyage without. Their deranged race for the Base Camp of the soul had concealed the outer world in a blizzard of self-deception. They were infatuated with The Search, and had slammed the Doors of Perception closed behind them.

Still, they had helped Henry and he felt no blame, just sad that they couldn't be here with him. Especially Karen, the most human of them all, who'd captured just a piece of his crumbling heart. She had given him a letter for later. 'Open it in the mountains and it'll open *You*,' she'd said.

He sat at the lakeside in the dwindling light and pulled out her letter. In it she said that he'd found his way inside her, that she loved him in a cosmic rather than sexual way. Henry felt pleased and piqued at the same time; he'd rather have gone for the carnal than the cosmic right then but knew that he wasn't ready yet to get married again. His mother's voice still whispered hot in his ear.

It was a friendly letter and made him feel maybe he'd been too hard on the folks in Calgary, and a little blind where Karen was concerned. Shame. Round the side of the letter was a coiled snake, pointing to the top left-hand corner. At the tail of the snake were the words 'Welcome' and 'Look through the Windowpane'. At the head was stuck a tiny three-millimetre square of gelatine film with 'Say hallo to the Mountains for me' written round it in tiny letters. Henry smiled to himself and knew that when the time was right he would do just that. Meanwhile he slipped the letter back in his pocket and went back to the bunkhouse to get his guitar out and sing 'The Blue Canadian Rockies' again.

Two days later the time was right. Henry had clambered round both sides of the lake and on to the bottom of the glacier. The feeling of having come home was still overwhelming. Now he needed to get up high and look long distances. He'd discovered the mountain to climb and now it looked like he had the perfect day. Bright, pale-blue sky with cotton-wool clouds racing across it. Now was the time.

He stripped the little square from Karen's letter, flicked it into his mouth and started to walk along the rocky path that lead to the Little Beehive, a mountain which was supposed to have a staggering view over the valley that ran along the east side of the Great Divide. The path came out of the forest very quickly and headed upwards. As it zig-zagged up the side of the Little Beehive, Lake Louise fell away below him and the further away it went the more intense and opalescent the colour became. Distances stretched into dizzying perspectives and more and more mountain tops came to join him, peeking over ridges as he trudged on up out of the Louise valley. He stopped for a moment and a wombat waddled over and sat on his sneakers. They looked at each other for a while. Henry struggled to get his camera out and as he pointed it at the wombat he suddenly realized the acid was hitting hard and fast. He grunted at the animal which grunted back. He had been looking down at the wombat on the ground for some time and had forgotten he was on a goat track on the side of a mountain. When he finally looked up and started to climb again his legs were jellying and the Rockies were beginning to swirl. Ah, well, thought Henry, onwards and upwards, as he clambered up the side of the granite whirlpool, onwards and upwards.

By the time he got to the top Henry had lost every bone in his body. The Rockies had become Dervishes, dancing frenziedly around him and waving the clouds in the sky like handkerchiefs over their heads. The whole damn mountain range was hootin' and hollerin' round him and all he could do was stand there and breathe. He didn't even have the strength to sit down.

'Hi, there, how're ya doin'?'

Henry's heart jumped into his throat. He had thought he was alone on his mountain top and was certain he wasn't going to be able to deal with a human being right now. He turned his head and saw an old man behind him, standing beside a little glass-walled house. He hadn't seen anything earlier, but then he was peaking just as he got to the peak. He scrambled through the last unsplintered remnants of his mind and remembered that because of the panoramic view from Little Beehive there was a Forest Ranger look-out hut at the top. Deep breath. Henry grunted.

'Looked like hail, or even a little early snow first thing this mornin', but it seems Mother Nature has jes' rolled back the clouds to give us another fine day.'

Henry grunted, longer this time.

'Like to come on in 'n have some coffee? There's a pot on the stove.'

Henry grunted again and wobbled towards the glass house. The old man turned and limped into the cabin; he had a gammy leg and looked like he must be the Ranger. He seemed to be tall and stooped with dark hair, and wearing Brown Things. Henry couldn't tell much beyond that, so he just followed him in gingerly, wiping some foam from his lips. He knew his eyes must have looked like they were out on stalks, but he could deal with that. The foam, he thought, would've been a dead giveaway. Even here at the centre of the cyclone, riding the top of the mountain like it was a galloping horse, his mind flailing and unable to do anything more than grunt, Henry was a survivor. Although it was only his second trip he had an awareness that made him able to deal with people at a time when he'd much rather be talking to rocks. A few times that day his awareness would tip over into raging paranoia and he'd find himself surfing along on a tidal wave of fear. If he lost his balance he knew the demons waiting jabbering in the sea of his subconscious would pull him down into a murderous madness that he'd probably never survive. But he had no intention of becoming an acid casualty—

Hey, now, just hold it right there, Hutt. If you go on like this, it'll be this book that is the casualty. What're you trying to do fer Chrissakes? Lose all of Hank's fans? This is turning into some kinda goddamn freaky drug manual.

Look, Colonel, you wanted the true life story warts and all—

Warts, OK, but do we need the running sores as well?

Look, Colonel, I'm only telling the folks what Hank told me, *as he told it*. And you said you wanted nothing but the truth, that I shouldn't hold back anything important in Hank's life, and this day in the Rockies is *essential*. We're going to find out how he got to be called Hank and why he got involved in Indian mythology.

Indian WHAAT! What the hell's this mythowhatever got to do with Country and Western? And how many Indians're gonna buy this book anyways, have you thought of that? Give the folks what they expect, dickhead. Don't rock the goddamn boat before it's even launched.

OK, OK, OK, you want me to turn him into John Denver, then? *That* kind of Rocky Mountain High? Is that what you want?

Now, c'mon, son, no need to go that far. Just you remember we've still got the American rights and too much of this Hippieshit ain't gonna help sales there one little bit. Just straighten up a tad, that's all.

49

Colonel, this is neither the time nor the place for a script conference. Just lay off, will you? You remember, too, that I've got a contract for this, *You signed it, right?*

OK, OK. But I'm watching you. And contracts can be broken . . .

'Sugar? Milk?'

Henry grunted, waved his hand and feebly shook his head.

'As it comes? OK, that's how I like mine too. *Just like life – as it comes.*' The old boy chuckled. 'I'm the Forest Ranger up here. Name's Stringer, Len Stringer. Good to meet you.' He held out his hand and Henry took it, concentrating every fibre of his arm to do a convincing shake. A man who can shake hands is worth ten who can talk, he thought, and squeezed hard.

'Jeez, you got a good grip there, son, you're gonna be all right.' Henry pulled what he hoped was a friendly smile, grunted and stuck his face in his coffee. Tables ran along all four walls of the little cabin, covered with survey maps, pens, rulers, binoculars, a telescope, all the paraphernalia of a look-out. Through the glass the whole astonishing view stretched from far right to even further left, especially astonishing for young Henry as the mountains were still racing around like they were water-skiing on a twenty-foot swell. He waved his arm slowly across the view and grunted quizzically. Len seemed to understand the question perfectly.

'Yep, I'm up here all summer,' he said, gazing sightlessly into the sky, 'lookin' out fer forest fires. Got a phone here, see, and I can let 'em know just as soon as I see anything. Been doin' this the last fifteen years.'

Henry grunted again and with a supreme effort raised his eyebrows and pointed at the floor.

Len was right there again. 'Nope, I don't get lonesome, no sir. I'm up here with the Lord and the eagles, and then there's a few folks come up like yerself. Mind you, some of 'em talk so damn much, you can't get a word in edgeways. Talk the hind legs off a jackrabbit.'

Henry grunted and checked his mouth for foam again. Strung out with Len Stringer.

'Makes you glad at times to be up here alone. Twenty years ago I did the loggin'. That's how I got this.' Henry grunted as Len tapped his leg. "Course, guy like you'd do well loggin'. *Don't say a lot, you hear a lot more.* It's the guys that keep yakkin' get the trees fall on 'em. It's true, they don't see what's goin' on around 'em and those trees're droppin' all the time. Or they fall off the logs goin' down the river.' Grunt. 'I ain't kiddin', it happens. I seen a man fall off a log, another log come right up behind 'im, rrrip! took his nuts right off.' Henry winced and nearly formed a word. 'Clean off. Poor bastard. Then I got this leg here not watchin' and a tree come down kinda sideways. They're mean, try and take you out as they come down, try and take you with 'em. Can't blame 'em though, they must feel pretty pissed at bein' cut down in the first place.'

Henry went on grunting and Len carried on chatting for the next couple of hours. There was the logging, the Indians, the mountains and his mobile home down near Edmonton where he wintered. There was mountain medicine, forest fires, the railways, the goldrush. There were volcanoes, eagles, brown bears and grizzlies. Most of all the Indians. Len knew a lot about the Indians and loved them. Said he was one-eighth Assiniboine 'on my Godmother's side'. They both staggered out into the fresh air now and then and looked over the edge to the great sweep of the valley running alongside to the east of the Divide, the spine of the Rockies, and Len pointed out the railway and the road and the light- and dark-shaded patches of forest where there had been a forest fire sixty years before. Sixty years is young for a forest and it showed.

Sixty years is young for a man, too, if Len Stringer was anything to go by. Over the couple of hours Len had told his stories, the Rockies had calmed their most ferocious skirling and skidding about down to a sedate, almost-normal, slow waltz and Henry could see that Len had weathered well. He was tall and thick-set with the stoop of a man who liked to hear what shorter people were saying to him. Dark haired, his brown eyes shone out of his leathery face from under thick trustworthy eyebrows. At least that's what Henry thought they were but then Henry wanted to trust everyone he met. He didn't see the second translucent eyelid that would flicker down from under the top one like a crocodile's nictitating membrane whenever Len would stop talking and gaze back into the sky for a while. He could see, though, that Len was well preserved, baked by the sun and cooled by the wind, a man at one with his surroundings.

At last Henry found he could just about speak again. Right then, as if he knew, Len asked him a direct question for the first time that couldn't be answered with a wave of a hand or a finger pointing at a mouth.

'What's your name, son?'

'Henry. Henry Hardman.'

'Is that right? Hell, I *knew* you reminded me of someone. You're the spittin' image of my second cousin Henry. Same nose, same way of walkin', same crazy eyes and same way of talkin'. He don't say too much neither. 'Cept we called him Hank, short for Henry. Hank.'

Henry thought about it for a moment. *Hank*. It sounded good, it felt right. Funny he'd never thought of it before. Although he'd been in

America for about three years now he still thought of Henry as an English name. Hank. It could have been Harry which he couldn't go with at all. Henry was hard enough. Hank. Hmmmm.

'Hardman. That's an Indian name. I know a Kwakiutl guy from BC called Hardman.'

'No. I'm . . . from . . . England,' stammered Henry, 'but I've heard . . . of the . . . Kwaki . . . utl . . . They carve . . . fantastic . . . totems and . . . their . . . Trickster . . . is a . . .Raven.'

'Yep, or sometimes a Mink, you're right there, son.' Len beamed, a great crooked grin. 'I didn't know you liked Trickster too.'

Rocky
☆
Mountain High

Trickster is the strongest universal myth around, one of the earliest ideas man ever conceived, and has survived almost unchanged over thousands of years all over the world, from primitive aboriginal to sophisticated civilized societies. Trickster is found in Chinese, Japanese, Indian and Semitic cultures. He is, as they say, one of the Big Ones.

In medieval Europe he was the Jester and gave rise to Punch and Judy, and to the Clowns. Henry had always loved the kindly destructiveness of clowns as a kid in Wangford but had not felt as close to them as he did to Trickster when he discovered him in Wisconsin.

☆ ★ ☆

While he was retreating from his marital battleground into the apple-pie music he loved so well, he started to sing some Country duets with his good friend in Sheboygan Falls, Kevin Nose. Kevin was short, dark and intense. His mother was Irish and his father was a Winnebago Indian. Kevin signed his name Kevin B. Nose because he didn't want people to know that B stood for Big. His father, grandfather and great-great-grandfather's names were Big Nose but they were all full-blood Winnebagos, and Big Nose was a noble name.

Kevin just couldn't cope with being Kevin Big Nose.

'An Irish Winnebago, makes me sound like a Catholic Mobile Home,' he complained. But he delighted Henry with stories of Trickster that he'd heard from his father.

Trickster is often an animal. In China it is Monkey who came down from Heaven and refused to behave himself on Earth. To many of the American Indian tribes it is Coyote. Trickster is amoral, destructive, slyly naïve, dumb and smart, and can't tell good or bad apart. He has no sense of values, moral or social, but out of his seemingly random madness comes order, and his destructiveness can be unwittingly constructive. He fools us *and* he can be fooled. He is a slave to his passions and appetites and has no sense of responsibility for what he does. He sounds like a bit of a Cosmic Psychopath, but out of his amorality comes new values. And then, just sometimes, Trickster *is* actually God, and plays the final trick on us.

After he and Henry'd had a good Delmore Brothers and Carter Family session, Kevin would settle down and transport Henry with strange stories he'd heard from his father.

'One day Coyote killed a buffalo and while his right hand was skinning it, his left hand started to pull it away. His right hand pulled it back and went on skinning it. His left hand pulled it away again, so his right hand, which had the knife, tried stabbing at his left to stop it. The left arm kept pulling the buffalo away. "Give that back," the right arm said, and kept slashing and jabbing at the left. With his left arm cut up and bleeding. Coyote howled "Why do I have to suffer so much? Why does it always happen to *me*?"'

'That's pretty strange, Kevin.'

'Well, if you think that's strange, Henry, how about this one . . . One day, Coyote took an elk's liver and made a vagina out of it, took the elk's kidneys and made them into breasts and slipped into a dress. He looked so pretty that the fox fancied him. He let the fox hump him, then the jaybird and then the nit; he became pregnant so he went to a village, married the chief and had four good-looking sons.'

'What's it all mean, Kevin?'

'You can never be sure, Henry,' said Kevin, 'with Trickster sometimes it's hard to tell.' There were other simpler stories like Trickster stealing fire from the Fire People, but giving it to the trees so that now everyone can make fire with firesticks. And Henry, oppressed and depressed by his life in Sheboygan Falls, identified strongly with the wildness of Trickster. As he found out more, he came across the Kwakiutl and found that their Trickster was a Raven . . .

☆ ★ ☆

'Yep, or sometimes a Mink, you're right there, son. Y'see, Raven is greedy for everything especially food. But Mink is greedy for everything especially women. Why, I didn't know you liked Trickster too.'

Henry looked up into Len's crooked grin and realized he was back in the glass house on top of a mountain on the Great Divide talking about Indians, forests, mountains and Prairies with an old guy with one good leg. He looked out through the glass walls, realized how high up he was and had a moment of freezing panic. 'People in glass houses shouldn't get stoned,' he thought to himself, and laughed aloud as the panic melted.

'That's right,' drawled Len, 'Trickster makes you laugh jes' to think about him . . . Sometimes he makes you think about laughing . . . Sometimes he gets so darn cussed, he jes' makes you *think*.'

They sat for a while in silence and thought about it all, about the monstrous majesty of Creation, its order and its chaos. They were staring through the glass wall at the sweeping touch of God's hand before them, when they both noticed what looked like a bird of some sort soaring across the valley below them. At first a speck, it grew and grew as it flew nearer and higher. As it caught the thermals coming up the side of Little Beehive, it rose with a silent stillness up towards them.

It was a giant, it was black and it made no noise.

'What the hell?' said Len. 'Is that a buzzard or an eagle or . . .' His voice trailed off as he grabbed a pair of binoculars and thrust a smaller pair at Henry. They both watched as the bird soared effortlessly nearer, as if it were homing in on them. Henry struggled putty-handed with his binoculars until he had jammed them up against his eyes and focussed on the great bird. It was pretty close by now and still rising. Len and Henry craned their heads back as it rose above them. Its vast wings hardly moved, just feathering a little at the tips and the outer trailing edges, tilting slightly to left and right as it soared on up. By now they could see that though it had a sharp curved beak like an eagle, it was no eagle and far too big for a buzzard. It had a bald white head and a scrawny, featherless neck, like the death's head of a vulture. But as it flew closer and closer over them it looked too *Regal* somehow, and certainly too big to be an ordinary vulture. At the base of its neck was a frill of white down before its brilliantly black body. Its great black wings had bright white bars along the front edge of its twelve-foot wing span—

'I don't believe it . . . Jesus Christ,' Len muttered under his breath, 'I just don't believe it. But it looks like it . . . but it can't be, no way, not up here.' Len had gone to the door and was looking straight up as the bird was now hovering about four hundred feet directly over them. Henry tottered over after him.

'Wha' . . . what . . . is . . . it?' he stammered.

Len screwed his eyes up, taking a final disbelieving look.

'Well, son, it ain't possible, so I'm probably wrong, 'cos it don't belong up here, and no one's ever seen one up here, 'cos it should be thousands of miles away down south in the Andes, but hell, boy, it sure as hell looks awful like a condor to me.'

As Len said this the giant bird peeled over to one side and circled down towards them. Barely fifty feet above them it turned inwards with the merest flick of its wingtips, ducked its head and appeared to be staring them in the eyes as it slid straight over their heads. Henry stared straight back and found himself looking into a long eye of the most brilliant purple, a purple eye gleaming out of a repulsively naked head.

'It is, dammit, it's a goddam condor, a goddam *condor* fer Chrissakes an' damn! Where's my camera?' Len lurched back into the little house when SSSSSSHHKWELTCHHESSS, a huge stripe of birdshit splattered down the glass side of the house and dripped on to the mountain top. By the time Len came out with his camera it was all that was left of the bird which had wheeled round south and was now just a speck heading for Banff. Henry was lying catatonic on his back staring at the sky. Len kneeled down beside him on his good leg and patted Henry's face.

'C'mon, Hank, c'mon son, it's OK, the condor's gone, it just shit on us a bit is all.' Henry was about to remind Len that he was *Henry*, not Hank when he felt the warmth and reassurance of Len's voice. Hank. Hmmm. Hank. Mmm, it sounded all right. Hank Hardman. He ran it round his head a couple of times and he liked it. Anyhow, he figured, if he could have a condor shit on him in the Blue Canadian Rockies, then *anything* could happen. And nothing was going to be the same when he went back *down* the mountain, so why not have a new name as well?

'Thanks, Len, I'm fine, just fine.' He raised himself up on his elbow and rubbed his eyes.

'Hey, that's the first time you've said my name,' said Len smiling broadly, 'an' I got yours wrong, mixed you up with Cousin Hank, when you told me you stuck with straight ol' Henry. Your fault fer looking the image of him, though.'

'Listen, Len, I was raised in a village in the East of England, and I've been here in the States for a couple of years trying to track down my dad who left home years ago. I'm trying to piece a few things together, to understand what's going on. Already I'm not the kid who got beaten up at school, who got Tizer and Fling squirted all over him during the morning breaks, I'm *not Henry* anymore. Hank'll do nicely, thank you.' As Hank was saying this, Len sank backwards, his eyes popping, like he'd seen a ghost. He was staring at Hank's mouth, open for the first time since he arrived on the summit several hours before.

'You've got the same teeth, exactly the same teeth as Cousin Hank,' he croaked. 'You don't jes' have the same walk and same crazy eyes, you've got the *same goddamn snaggle teeth* as him. I don't know what's going on. I, maybe I've been up here on Beehive too long. I, I need a break. I, maybe I'm seeing things. This is crazy, that can't have been a condor here over Lake Louise and your teeth can't be that snaggled.'

'Hold on, Len,' Hank had his hands on Len's shoulders as the old boy started babbling and needed to be calmed down in his turn. 'That *was* a condor you saw back there, and,' Hank bared his teeth and looked straight at Len, 'I *am* as snaggled-toothed as they come.'

They sat and looked at each other for a while, silent and hardly blinking.

'You know what, Hank, I'd say Trickster has been here with us today.'

'You know what, Len, I'd say he's still with us right now. And you're sitting in a pile of condor shit.'

Len felt behind him with his hand, looked at it, looked at Hank and they both burst out laughing. They laughed and they laughed until the tears streamed down and the sun started to dip over the ridge of the seven glaciers at the head of Lake Louise.

'It's getting kinda late, son. If you've got nothing special to pull you down to ground level right now, you can stay up here the night,' said Len. 'I've got a camp bed I can put up for you and you'd be welcome to watch the night fly right past your head. The dawn looks good coming up over the other side of the valley.'

Hank needed little convincing. He was still out of his head but the trials and the demons of earlier in the day had mellowed with the setting sun and in the end it was two days later before he left that little mountaintop. That night Hank saw his first Northern Lights; Len told him the Indians said it was the flashing of the spirits of Medicine Men in combat and that's pretty much how it looked to Hank.

Over the next two days Len told Hank a lot of things the Indians said and Hank took it all in. He talked of the Piegans and Assiniboine. He spoke of the Kutenai and Okanagan from the other side of the Divide and how they wore bear claws to absorb Bear Virtue, a kind of paternal warrior spirit. He said how, to the coastal-island Haida people, a Heaven Bear stood where the sun rose every morning and a great pillar supports the sky where it sets.

He told Hank of the Athabascan Beaver tribe from the Peace River in Alberta who said that in the beginning the roles of animals and people were reversed; gigantic animal ancestors roamed the woodlands, hunting and eating Indians until a great hero called Saya learned the Medicine Songs of the animals and turned their power against them, making the animals smaller and the Indians their hunters. By learning any animal's Medicine Song, an Indian will be given some of its natural power and the ability to prophesy and to heal. The Beavers' Dreaming Songs are sung by their Shamen, their medicine men, who as *Swans* have the power to fly across the Great Divide to that other world where symbols become reality, and to take their tribe with them to that place, pulling the tribe together in harmony with themselves and with their environment.

Hank, who had always felt out of kilter with his family, was drawn in by the Beavers' songs and saw in them some hope for his future. I suppose it's a start, but poor fool, thinking that two nights on a mountaintop could bring him lifelong peace and harmony just like that . . . After all, he wasn't Moses and Len's stories weren't carved on tablets of stone.

That's good, Sam, that's good. Let's have more of the biblical references, we've still got the American market. That's what this book needs, a bit more Bible in it. And less of this Indian mythowhatever crap. That lot are too drunk to buy this book anyhow.

Colonel, will you just horn out? The Indians are a noble people and . . .

Noble my ass. They're a bunch of sponging, whining alkies who take our welfare handouts and drink 'em all away. We give 'em money, land to live on and what do they want? More land, that's what.

But it was their land in the first place, we took it from them.

Who says it was theirs? What do they know about real estate? Did they ever have contracts???

Colonel, it's not a question of contracts, it's . . .

And what did they do with the land, huh? Did they build railroads and great cities? Did they bring civilization? No, it was the white man who Made America Great. It was the white man who did all this and listen, don't tell me nothing about carving on tablets of stone, I'm talking about the people who carved the faces of four of the world's greatest leaders into the side of a mountain. Now *that's* what I call harmony with nature.

Oh, come on, Colonel, that's just crazy talk. All they did was turn the mountain into a gigantic paperweight. Anyway, please, let's leave the Indian Problem to another time, yes? Just count the money.

I would if there was any to count, but the way you're going, I won't even be able to count my blessings.

All right, Colonel Frank, all right.

Potlatch

HANK: *OK, Doc, tell me how you felt when you saw me in Vancouver?*

SAM: I'd been in BC for about a month. I was staying and working with a Hippie self-help agency called Kool Aid. I was helping at the Free Clinic where they appreciated the bit of homeopathy I knew. I read an article about your band in the local alternative newspaper, the *Georgia Straight* I think it was. It sounded pretty whacky – a semi-Kwakiutl C & W band. The name had pot in it, didn't it?

HANK: *Potlatch. A Chinook word which means Gift. A Potlatch became a Kwakiutl party, a feast where they would give and destroy gifts.*

SAM: What do you mean destroy?

HANK: *Exactly that. The Kwakiutls were obsessed with wealth and power. So the bigger the party, of course, the more wealthy the person. But then as well as giving gifts, everyone would bring some favourite item to destroy. They'd build a big fire in the middle of the party and people would toss on their best clothes or furniture. The more valuable and loved the item, the greater the Gift. So if you barbequed, say, your favourite dining-room suite, then you were really rocking and people thought you were a real smart guy. I went to a real Potlatch once when they incinerated a grand piano.*

SAM: Ha! Music lovers.

HANK: *Uh huh. So I'd fallen in with a bunch of Kwakiutls who were into Country music and we formed the Hardman Tribe, we called it first, but as we got stranger, we changed it to Potlatch. We were getting destructive, too, taking some favourite songs and blowing them apart. We were big Zappa and Beefheart fans.*

SAM: Yes, you were very whacky. I first saw you in a club in Gastown, and when I came in you were doing a fractured psychedelic version of

59

Tennessee Wig Walk, one of the stupidest songs of all time. It was a cross between Cousin Jody and Syd Barrett when he started Pink Floyd, with two of you dressed in bird masks, gigantic beaks, I remember, doing a backwards chicken dance on the brink of madness.

HANK: *Oh, right. The Slippery Sisters, Melody and Valerie, were backing singers and dancers. They were being Raven there. You see, Trickster again. We were very involved in Totems, Trickster and the Potlatch idea of destroying artefacts that you hold too dear. I always loved Pete Townshend for smashing some of his most beautiful guitars and thought he was probably a Kwakiutl ... He certainly looks like a Totem ... Anyway, Melody Slippery and her sister Valerie did great vocals and bizarre dances. Melody's best friend Serena Sunshine—*

SAM: Oh, come on Hank.

HANK: *No, for real, honest. They have the most wonderful names, you don't need a stage name if you're Kwakiutl. Anyway, so how did you feel then?*

SAM: Pretty disoriented for a while, mostly from all that insanity, I just wondered where I had seen you before, your face looked awfully familiar, but I didn't make the connection that we looked alike. Not until I made my way in closer and even then not at first. You don't recognize a double unless someone points them out to you because you don't think you look like *that*. And then you started howling, doing a werewolf's full-moon version of 'He'll Have to Go', and I saw the teeth, I saw your gap and I felt a shiver like I had just walked on my own grave.

HANK: *That's very poetical, nicely put, Doc. A pity it took another four years before we met.*

SAM: Well, I don't know. I was so shaken up by seeing you then that I left town the next day. I thought I'd go and calm down in California. I thought at last I'd head for that easy-going West Coast love and peace that I'd heard of for years. Seeing you howling your heart out made me decide I had to go *right then*.

HANK: *And did you find what you want?*

SAM: Ha! Do we ever?

California
☆
Dreamin'

It looked like this was going to be my first night under the stars for a while. I watched the late-afternoon sun pitching down behind the tall forest and started to get used to the idea. My last lift had dropped me about an hour ago. I'd walked and thumbed a bit but no one had stopped. Well, so what if I had to sleep outside on my first night in California, where better than here in the Mendocino Redwoods? The sky looked clear and the sunset was beginning to splash over the treetops. It was warm and, though I had no camping equipment, I was looking forward to a night out in the woods. The forest floor was crisp and dry because there had been a bit of a drought, with no rain at all for the previous six weeks. Since I'd seen my howling *doppelgänger* up in Vancouver and left in a state of shock, I'd ambled down US1, along the Washington and Oregon coast, wondering at the ruggedness of it all and staying in a succession of forgettable motels. Though I'd seen the glinting of seals basking in the sun on the rocks just out from the coast, I didn't feel as if I'd got off the road yet.

Right then a classic VW Microbus came trundling round the bend, with a huge smile like Batman's Joker painted on the front. *These are my people*, I thought, as the bus heaved over and stopped. The driver leaned over the woman in the front beside him.

'Hey there, where're you going, man?'

'South. Just south.'

'In a hurry?'

'No, I'm just taking my time. Just rambling.'

'Ha, far out, man. Jump in.'

I tossed Eric's backpack and my guitar into the back through the open side door and jumped in. A young couple, Ben and Alice, were in the bus with their two children. Poor kids had to suffer the stigma of the Sixties' names. The girl was Sequoia, the Giant Tree, and the boy was called Tao, the mega-negative Chinese form of Buddhism. We all said Hi! and found out that they were on their way back to the commune in the Redwoods a few miles down the road. Did I need somewhere to stay for the night? I could stop by with them. I thought about the bears shitting on me as I slept in the woods.

'Far out,' I murmured, 'that'll be dandy. So what do you folks do up here?' Alice turned round.

'We keep it together, day by day, we study some and we think about *IT ALL*.' She smiled serenely.

'Yeah, we've moved up here to get our heads together,' said Ben. 'We live and work at an institute for the study of non-violence here in the woods, called Mankind. Come and *Be* with us for a while. It's good.'

I'd spent a long time in Canada recently with people who spoke their minds. Certainly in Saskatchewan the people were like the Irish or the Aussies and had no *side*, and everything could be taken at face value. Like Hank, I'm a bit naïve and have difficulty translating things folks tell me. I like to believe that people tell the truth and even if I get an intuitive twinge, a kind of mental stitch, I usually pay no attention and accept what I'm being told. I'd be useless in politics and can cope with Rock 'n' Roll only by believing absolutely nothing. The face value of the music business is the Bulgarian lev of the international currency market.

As this was my first night in California I had not yet grasped the multiple layers of the Californian psyche. I still thought that a searcher after truth was truthful, that someone seeking the peace that passeth all understanding was in a state of perpetual bliss. Studying non-violence sounded reasonable enough, a bit quixotic but commendable. I never stopped to think *why they needed to study it*. My first mistake.

I stayed for a week with the Mankind mob, who had made an idyllic settlement right in the heart of the Redwoods about a mile up a dirt track off the main road. They had a group of log cabins spread out under the towering trees with a central eating-and-meeting cabin and a few small organic allotments in a clearing. The serenity of the scene was held together by the crackling and whispering sounds of the reverberating forest.

There were about thirty people in the community, spread over three generations. Most were twenty to thirty but there were lots of kids and a couple in their seventies. They were proud of this generational span and maintained it gave a more balanced outlook on things, as they had interwoven into the community the wisdom of age and the responsibility of children.

The days passed non-violently, even peacefully, with folks doing handicrafts like woodwork and metalwork, reading, having seminars, growing vegetables and meditating. I sat under the Redwoods and played my guitar a lot. They seemed a little nervous of a doctor out on the road with a guitar and I always felt like an outsider; it might have been the lust boiling in my eyes for I had not lost myself with someone for longer than I liked to remember. But I was chary too and a mite confused by various Vibes that were flying around.

Alice and Ben were still very friendly as was their mate Jeannie who came and sat under the tall trees and talked to me a lot. She even sang with me a bit. I hoped that she fancied me but every time I'd give her the eye she would lower her voice conspiratorially almost to a whisper.

'Alice wants to speak with you.'

'No problem. I'm here, she's welcome.'

'Yes, but she *really* wants to speak to you.'

'Well, tell her that's fine by me, Jeannie. Anytime.'

From Jeannie's tone it sounded like Alice wanted to talk to me as a doc, perhaps for some advice about PMT or period pains or suchlike. I left Alice to ask me herself. The days went by quietly and in the evenings we'd all cook and eat and then sing together with a couple of bongos and flutes joining my guitar. Still it didn't rain and still Alice wouldn't tell me what was on her mind. At least not until the following Saturday night after we'd all eaten and sung.

I'd gone back to my cabin and was sitting on the ground outside, back to the wall, staring at the stars which were firm and bright in the black sky. Alice came out of the night and sat down on her haunches beside me. We shared a few pleasantries about the stars and the drought. She told me how they were even thinking of getting a rain-maker to call down the precious water from the cloudless skies. Then at last she told me what was on her mind.

It turns out that Jeannie, Ben and I were all on her mind. It turns out that in the name of sexual freedom, of non-possessive Universal Love, to root out the great dragon Jealousy, Ben had been knobbing Jeannie stupid for the last year. To show that there was nothing hidden, and because he was Totally Honest in his relationship, *he told Alice everything*. They'd all three tried going together but that didn't work out. It was Ben who couldn't handle it in the end. He couldn't take the responsibility of deciding who he would come with, which woman he would honour with his orgasm. Bit of a prick.

She didn't seem hurt or resentful and just looked very pretty, dark haired and fragile featured.

'Are you still friends with Jeannie?'

'Sure, and Ben too. I haven't stopped loving them. As long as they're loving to me and to Sequoia and Tao. She scratched dreamily at the ground between her legs with a stick. 'We're all friends. I'd like to be friends with you too.' She smiled slowly, turned her head and looked round at me out of the corners of her eyes. 'You know what I'm saying.'

I certainly did and was very pleased to hear it as she slipped her arm through mine. Fair's fair, I thought, and free is free. If it's OK for him it has to be the same for her. At least, that's what I'd always thought. There's geese and there's ganders and there's always sauce to go around. And it *was* Saturday night in the Mendocino Redwoods. So we whispered our way through the woods to my cabin.

Just as we stopped rolling and tumbling around, the rains started. It wasn't just rain, it was *Rains*. Plural. Lots of them, torrential, a deluge, cats and dogs having a hoedown, polka-ing away noisily on the roof. We laughed about being rainmakers and fell fast asleep in each other's arms.

The next thing I know I'm curled up in bed in pain, my face in my hands. My hands are wet and ow! my head hurts and my mouth hurts and *ow*! cough! my chest HURTS! What's happening? I'm confused and shocked and a minute ago I was warm and asleep and now *Ow*! it still hurts and what's this on my hands, its sticky and . . .

'Wassgoin'on? Wassappenin'? Alice are you all ri—'

'I'm fine, Sam. You'd better go. Here, get dressed. Here's your pants.' As Alice helped me out of bed and into my jeans I could hear a mumbling from outside the cabin. I couldn't make it out and besides I was more interested in why my head and chest were hurting so bad and why my hands were covered in what seemed like blood which seemed to be coming from over my eye and out of my mouth. What *was* going on? What wa— and then I understood the droning voice outside.

'Get him out of there. Get him out. Get him out . . . NOW.'

Ben was thumping on the cabin wall as he chanted on. I still wasn't quite sure where I was but whoever I was, I knew I wasn't wanted.

'Goodbye Sam. Take care of yourself, my love. I'll find you somehow sometime. Now go.' *Ow*! That hurt, that hug.

Reeling through the rain I was still dazed and confused. It was bucketing down through the cold, grey morning light and I was soaked in seconds. The great trees had a steely-grey unfriendliness about them that seemed to be saying 'I told you so.' With each sloshing step through the mudbath that had been the dirt track the pain in my side got worse and the fog in my mind got clearer.

'*Oowww!*' I cried aloud as I stumbled on a root. I put my pack and guitar down and felt gingerly over my right eye and my right rib cage. *Ow*! It's sore. It felt like I had one or two broken ribs and when I brought my hand down from my eye it was covered in blood which streamed away between my fingers in the rain. My watch said quarter to five. What *is* all this? What's just happen— and then Ben came into my mind. The boiling rage outside the cabin. We must conquer jealousy. But if you go off with any bastard, I'll conquer *him*. Ha! I laughed out loud. *Ouch!* It hurt to laugh.

I grabbed my things and staggered on through the mocking woods. What a bastard, eh? The whole jigsaw was beginning to fall into place piece by painful piece.

It was five in the morning.

It was pissing down.

I'd just been beaten up in my sleep.

And the only colour I could see in the grey early-morning light seeping through the treetops was the red blood oozing across my hand. Sexual freedom! Freedom for who? What a bunch of horse-shit double standards. Mankind!? *Man-bastard* is more like. *Ouch!* That still hurts and I'm soaked and where am I going?

Then, in a siding off the mudbath path, I saw the VW van. I decided to get out of the wet for a while so I went over to the van, crawled in and curled up. Who cares if they find me? Let him just try to have a go again . . . I'll be awake next time and I'm not too strong but I can fight dirty . . . I could knee him in the bollocks, no problem . . . What a bastard, eh . . .? Man-fucking-kind . . .

Listen, Doc, I've told you already that this is a family book. Do you have to use all this low-life language? It ain't gonna help the US sales none.

Look, Colonel, with all due respect, what do you know about the modern publishing world?

I know enough to know that it's made up of goddamn UNITS like anything else and if you keep this crap up you're not gonna shift any units at all.

OK, Colonel, OK. I'll check it out with my publisher and if she says it's just filth I'll cut it out. But I *was* in a lot of pain at the time, and that's how you talk when things hurt.

All right, Doc, I'll believe you this time. But don't forget that a pain in the wallet is a lot worse than a headache, and aspirin don't help it none. Just get on with it and *keep it clean.*

When I woke up the rain had stopped, the sky had cleared and the eight o'clock sun was scattering emeralds through the glistening canopy of dripping leaves. I'd have enjoyed the visionary beauty of it a whole lot more without the hammer in my head and the knife in my side, smug reminders of that murderous madness of a couple of hours earlier. *Oouch!* all right, I know I've only got myself to blame. *Oooww!* OK, OK, I should've seen it coming a mile off.

I eased myself painfully out of the van and straightened up slowly. I put both my hands on either side of the painful spot in my chest and squeezed my ribcage. *Eeoooowwwch!* Yep, that's broken ribs all right. I pressed an imaginary poultice to my whinging chest as I crept round the van to check myself in the wing mirror.

Jesus! I looked a mess. My lips were cut and puffed up, my right eye had an inch-long gash over it and was blackening up nicely and my hair was thickly matted with blood. Nice. You'll get a lot of lifts looking like that, I thought. I stumbled down to the creek and stuck my head into its swollen waters. When I'd got all the blood out of my hair and washed the mud off my boots I went back to the van to get out a fresh pair of jeans. Half an hour later I was picking my way down the track keeping a slightly paranoid black eye out for any student of non-violence who might be lurking in the undergrowth.

As I got to the main highway I remembered seeing a redneck in an Oregon bar a few days before. He looked like a trucker or a logger or some such and was busy chatting up a woman who was on the wrong side of a few dry martinis and threatening to spill out of her low-cut dress any minute.

He'd almost got to home base when he came out with the clincher:
'*Are you married, hon?*'
'*No,*' he said, '*but the Wife is.*'

I AIN'T MARRIED BUT THE WIFE IS

I knew a honky-tonkin' fool
A new girl every night
He always stuck to his golden rule
And never saw the same girl twice.
He loved them fat and he loved them thin
He loved them night and day
And if they saw his wedding ring,
Here is what he'd say

I ain't married, no sirree,
I'm just a man in a family
Free as a bird in a tall pine tree
I ain't married but the wife is.

He had a wife who never asked
Just what he did at night
He had a life so cut and dried
His pleasure sewn up tight
He had his women organized
Like puppets on a string
And if his heart got broken
He'd never feel a thing.

I ain't married, no sirree,
I'm just a man in a family
Free as a bird in a tall pine tree
I ain't married, I ain't married
I ain't married but the wife is.

Hank Wangford © Bucks Music and $incere $ongs

☆ ★ ☆

The lifts came thick and fast. The sunglasses over the shiner must have given me an attractive beach-boy effect and no one guessed that I was the Refugee from The Love Triangle. I got to San Francisco, black-eyed and not quite bushy-tailed, by four that afternoon. I was still in pain and a bit spaced out from my *Appointment with Destiny* only hours before. Breathing hurt but I couldn't really ease up on that too much. I just took short rapid shallow breaths and made do.

Once in the city, I had to make contact with a lawyer who was working in a bar, to get somewhere to stay for a while. His wife was the best friend of Shirley Donaldson who I'd been stepping out with in London just before I left for the Canadian flatlands. Eric was the guy who went into the sunset, in my place, with Shirley, and left me his backpack. Confused?

Not as confused as I was standing in Mooney's Bar, with my guitar and Eric's backpack, trying to catch the bartender's eye. I've always been pathologically uncharismatic with bartenders and waiters and stood there waiting for a while behind a line of drinkers hunched over the bar. I was wearing my bright-red Rose Valley Fire Department club jacket and despite all the dramas of the day was feeling quite exhilarated to be in San Francisco at last. The hunchback in front of me turned round slowly and looked at me.

'You Doctor Sam?'

My hands shot reflexly for my wounds. I stood there with my left hand over my splintered ribs, my right guarding my eye. My breathing took a rain check.

'Mmy-yes.'

He leaned forward. 'I think I should tell you you're not too welcome round these parts.'

If ever I was going to get asthma, this was it.

The man just turned back round on his chair and left me there wheezing. I don't even remember squeaking to the bartender, Larry the lawyer, or introducing myself, or getting the key from him for the flat round the corner.

As I wandered out of Mooney's I was completely gobsmacked, dumbstruck. Was I a guinea-pig in some bizarre CIA secret brainwashing experiment? What was going on? Why are all these Californians threatening me? Should I have worn a flower in my hair to come to San Francisco? Would they have liked that better? What about Peace and Love? *What is going on?* I felt as confused as Van Morrison.

Sitting in Larry the lawyer's flat I ran it all through again. This was too much like western movies, as if these people had lived too close to Hollywood all their lives.

> *This bar ain't big enough for both of us.*
> *This town ain't big enough for both of us.*
> *This woman ain't big enough for both of us.*

They were all a bunch of cowboys and I appeared to be the rodeo clown. It was my turn in the barrel. Here I was in San Francisco, it seemed like at the end of a quest, a retarded tourist on a daytrip to a time I knew had already died, and I knew no one except the friend of an ex-girlfriend and her legal-eagle bar-keep husband. And a cowboy in an Irish bar. I couldn't let that lot go; the heavy air of threat would just fester and spoil if I didn't face it again.

So I decided to go back to Mooney's to check it out. Things hadn't changed a lot. Hunchbacks were still knocking back drinks and the lights were low. I stood and waited for either the barman or another death threat. The barman ignored me and a dark-haired man in front of me swung round. He was relaxing in an old sports shirt, a cuffed pair of loafers and brown trousers.

''R you Doctor Sam?'

I wasn't carrying a six-gun so I reached for my ribs again. He saw the answer panicking in my gaping eyes.

'I'm John Donaldson. Shirley's husband.'

That's great, isn't it?

He's going to kill me. This is it.

His hand snaked out towards me and I jumped back into some kind of feeble attempt at a karate crouch. But there was nothing sharp or shiny in his hand and all he wanted to do was to shake mine. 'Let me buy you a drink,' he said, 'if you can stay for a while.'

So we sat for a while and drank a bit and he bent my ear. Somehow it seems my name had got linked with the reason Shirley split although I had met her eighteen months and a few boyfriends after they had broken up. The story was that *she had left him for me* and evidently the whole bar knew about it and had lived through it, helping him in his pain, for the last few months.

That was pretty easily cleared up so John just heaved in and gave me the whole life story, their marriage, the good, the bad and the ugly. He told me about his family, his mother, his brother who was gay and such a worry. He cried about his job; he'd just lost his lectureship at Hamburger University where he taught McDonalds' arts of packaging and rapid delivery. He was pointing out to students that there were no lectures on nutritional content. He spoke of the shitty things he'd done, how he'd cheated on Shirley, but how he still loved her, how he knew she was the only one, the whole damn psychodrama. He cried a lot. After two hours of this he stood up, shook me gratefully by the hand, thanked me from his heart for all my help and walked out.

In a daze, I watched him go. I wondered what would have happened if he also had studied at an institute for non-violence. He might, I thought, have been just a tad less pussyfooting namby-pamby verbal with me. He might have taken all his repressions, guilt, hatred, sexual frustration and anger out on me. He could have held back a little less.

He might even, in a studiedly non-violent way, have beaten the shit out of me.

Battle in Seattle

It's a battle in Seattle in the early morning cold,
Now my friends have gone and Washington is making me feel old.

© $incere $ongs

A year after I discovered that all was not what it seemed in Northern California, Hank himself started off down the long road south. At five o'clock one morning he found himself in the Seattle bus station. A grim, grey uncompromising place, it was full of people waiting for a bus to nowhere. Some were sitting in their TeeVee chairs in a twenty-five-cent trance, staring sightlessly at the little screens sticking out of the armrest just a foot from their hollow eyes. The flickering screens drew pallid shadows across their empty faces, soaking up the last traces of spirit from their withered souls.

A pool of piss seeped out of a pile of rags lying on the floor, the only sign that a human being inside had lost even his last legs.

A woman wept alone but no one saw.

A cleaner moved a pile of dirt from one side of the station to the other, rested for a while then moved it back again.

Hank took some hope from a young couple in the middle of this mausoleum, oblivious to the dead and the undead around them, necking passionately and telling each other how incredible they were as if they were on the most romantic of moon-kissed, palm-fringed, desert-island beaches and not in the armpit of the American North-west coast. *The power of love*. It was probably that touch of humanity in the heartless

70

emptiness of the Seattle morning that kept Hank from jumping on another Greyhound and heading further south.

☆ ★ ☆

He had left Vancouver under a cloud after being there for over a year. By early 1973, the musical destructiveness of Potlatch had degenerated into some kind of spiritual slaughter as if they were all tossing their emotions and their feelings on to the communal Kwakiutl fire. The intensity that had taken them far into the dark and deviant heart of Tribal C & W now threatened to burn them all up.

Hank and the Slippery Sisters in particular turned in on themselves when Hank met Myrtle Moneybird, a Northern Woods Cree from Manitoba with a natural Country voice like Loretta Lynn, who is herself part Cherokee. He wanted Myrtle to join the group as lead singer but this upset the Slipperies. They had been happy singing bizarre duets and doing their wild Trickster dances to a North Pacific honky-tonk back beat, and didn't want anyone rocking their canoe. Their antagonism may well have been tribal, manning the barricades against a Woods Cree upstart who probably knew little of Trickster's intricacies in Kwakiutl mythology. More likely it was just straight jealousy, for Melody who had long carried a torch for Hank, could see him hankering after Ms Moneybird.

When they did gigs, Melody Slippery was the psychopathic Raven and wore a giant bird beak on her face in the traditional Kwakiutl way, doing a one-legged swooping dance as she sang backing vocals on Marty Robbins songs. Little sister Valerie was Mink, the sexy one, and she would jump out into the audience and wind the men up into a priapic frenzy with a lewdly erotic shimmy. Sometimes she would have a foot-long white radish and nudge men lecherously with it, jabbing at their arms, legs, bellies and heads. Back on stage, Valerie/Mink would roll the radish between her thighs and even lick the end lasciviously. Sometimes she would chew bits off and spit them at the wincing men. Then, with a double-sided knife fanning across it like a blur, she would hold the radish upright and carve it into a thousand slices with a big grin on her face.

Valerie and Melody were an important part of Potlatch, and they didn't want to be relegated to backing singers. They thought Hank was trying to ease into more straightforward Country and Western. They were right, and when Hank tried to insist on bringing in Myrtle, the Slippery Sisters just said No. They weren't going to have anyone else coming in and carving their radish for them. So they broke up with some bitterness and, by June of 1973, Hank decided to go south of the border, down Washington way.

Sitting in Seattle bus station he was still a bit shell-shocked, wondering whether to come or go. He always was a romantic and the two lovers decided him. It must have been an omen, for a Mexican woman he met just that afternoon was to become his third ex-wife.

Maria was one of those stunning black-haired, dark-eyed natural beauties who take your breath away without even trying. She was working on the check-out in a little supermarket Hank went into later that day, standing in for her friend Dolores who was sick. At that time Maria was studying at a beauticians' school every morning. The supermarket was a Mexican family affair which was lucky as Hank was on the lookout for some jalapeño peppers to burn out the taste of decay the bus station had left in his mouth.

At the check-out all he had was some jalapeños, a jar of hot sauce, some tortilla chips and a couple of bottles of Dos Equis. He was stopped in his tracks by Maria's flashing black eyes and entranced by her sweet dimpled smile. She admired his taste in food, so they talked awhile. They got around to music and found out they both sang and played. She had family and friends who were musos, too, so with a refreshing directness she asked him down to the local Mexican restaurant that night to eat, meet and greet some of the others.

Maria's eyes sparkled and she seemed quite unafraid to ask a stranger out to dinner on first meeting. Hank could see there were no strings attached and admired her simple self-confidence. She had an ingenuousness he felt very close to, for he himself had always had a touch of innocence about him. Her smile took him a million miles away from the desolation of that morning in the bus depot. Hank had no idea that he was going to eat with his future ex-wife that very night or that he would meet his new band. He was still in shock from Vancouver and wasn't realizing a lot, except that he was strongly drawn to Maria.

The restaurant was La Oveja Negra, the Black Sheep, and Maria introduced Hank to the waiters and to the chef. After the meal, when they discovered that they all shared a love for that ol' apple-pie Country 'n' Western as well as Texan conjunto and Rhythm 'n' Blues, they went upstairs and played themselves silly right through the night. The two waiters, Pepito and Chico, played guitar and bass, and the chef Steve – Estaban – was the drummer. Maria played fine fiddle and accordion. They were looking for a front man as none of them could really sing Country music. Hank couldn't really sing anything but that had never bothered him before. He was looking for a band so it all seemed to fit in serendipitously. In less than a week they had rehearsed and routined enough for a set and had had done their first gig in the Oveja Negra playing a rootsy, kind of rockabilly Tex-Mex Country.

They called themselves Hank Hardman's Cojones Grandes. Pepito was a flashy lead guitarist and sang beautifully liquid backing vocals with Chico, always in the Spanish style. Maria sang with a fine tugging cry in her voice and played fiery accordion. Things moved very fast. Within a month they had cracked the Washington State Mexican-restaurant circuit.

A month later, after a whirlwind romance, Hank and Maria got married. This may seem a trifle hasty for Hank after two disastrous marriages, but he was obviously captivated and inspired by Maria's forthright *why not?* attitude to life. Perhaps, he thought, third time lucky.

Perhaps, more typically, he didn't think at all.

The band seemed to accept the happy couple although Chico, who was Maria's second cousin, looked dark now and then. He wrote songs, alone and with Hank, so some new bilingual, and a few unilingual, songs came out.

Then one day a local business man called Frank Wangford came to see them playing at the Oveja Negra.

☆ ★ ☆

LOS CAMAREROS – THE SPANISH WAITERS

Frank Wangford was a regular visitor to La Oveja. Hardly surprising since it was one of the first Mexican restaurants he had bought a share in. He now had an interest in several, in and around Seattle. Like Hank, Frank loved Mexican food and particularly jalapeños. In fact with jalapeños he went beyond. He would eat raw chillies that would reduce lesser folks to ashes. He would chomp on those things until he was red eyed. So the chain of Mexican restaurants was just insurance. Make sure of his supply.

Frank liked to be known as *Colonel Frank*, from the time when he had been a full Colonel in the Peruvian Indians, a Survivalist group he founded in the Hippie backlash at the end of the Sixties. He still makes a good living out of teaching people how to live with Anthrax and does a reasonable trade in the Ethical Chemical Warfare Clothing business. His best item is still the Anthrax Suit with instructions on how deep to dig the pit to bury the infected sheep.

Colonel Frank has a broad portfolio.

He had a longstanding relationship with the Mexican population of Washington. Over the years he had helped many Mexicans come up north from their country to work in the States, organizing their trip through his own company TMA – Trans-Mexican Airlines – and taking care of them and any problems with immigration they may have had. If any of these ill-starred and often exploited people were abused or underpaid by heartless employers, Frank Wangford always pledged to fly them back across the border to their native country any time things got too hot.

With several other interests in import-export and real estate, Colonel Frank Wangford was a busy man. But his eyes were always on new horizons and he made time to come and listen to Hank and the band's music – and he was impressed. Hank, for his part, was put at his ease by Frank's sincerity. Frank talked fast and though he had no direct experience of managing music groups, he felt that his work in transporting much larger groups south of the border would help him in the hard-nosed and perhaps less than lovely world of showbiz. He also realized instinctively from the start that product was product whichever way you looked at it.

Hank was certainly captivated by Frank's enthusiasm and ideas and decided that he should give him a try as his manager. The Cojones Grandes seemed happy to go along with it and respected Frank's benevolent and philanthropic reputation. Hank was also a sucker for strange coincidences and loved the fact that Frank had the same name as his birthplace even though Frank's came from a different root, from Wangerooge off the coast of Germany, Wangerooge-Foord being 'Ford to the Island of Wangerooge', just as Wangford in Suffolk is 'Ford over the River Wang'. The Colonel had anglicized Wangerooge-Foord to disguise his Continental origins.

And, coincidentally, the first thing Frank wanted Hank to do was change *his* name. He was worried about people being offended by the dirty meaning, the double meaning. Hank looked puzzled when Frank told him this.

'What do you mean, dirty?'

'Well, you know, Hank, *Hardman* ... HARDMAN,' Frank said through clenched teeth, bending his arm and making a fist and shaking it, pumping it underneath the table in a manly way.

'Oh, I see. What should I call myself then?'

'Well, Hank, I thought that with my name and your hometown being the same, maybe *Hank Wangford* would sound good ... *Hank* ... *Wangford* ... Think about it. And it would keep it clean. Nothin' personal. It's just, well, *Hardman* ... well, you know what I'm saying.' He went on jabbing provocatively at the space under the table with his clenched fist as his eyebrows danced up and down his forehead. Then, almost as an afterthought, he jerked forward suddenly and mumbled into Hank's ear, 'And if we're registered as kin there *could* be advantageous tax savings. You never know.'

Hank didn't understand the tax business but liked the idea of the name. So, for a while, they became Hank Wangford's Cojones Grandes until someone unwittingly told Frank what *cojones* were. After an almighty row where Frank claimed they had betrayed him, they agreed to change the name to Hank Wangford and the Spanish Waiters.

But it was the beginning of the end. Hank was falling more and

The Hankerers. The first Wangford Band, in England, with the Hankerchiefs (or the Joderelles), in a Rustic Setting. I have lent Hank my dungarees with San Francisco flower petals embroidered down one leg. The boys – Norman, Roy and Andy – are looking proud of their new band uniform T-shirts. Sixties connoisseurs note AB's flares.

Roy, Hank, Norman and AB (note the flares again) rehearsing outside Hill Farm.

The Hankerchiefs, Ginny and Susie, and Hank having a last rehearsal in the wagon before the first gig at Bungay May Horse Fair.

The first gig, in the marquee at the Horse Fair. Susie Cruise, the Vera Lynn of the North Sea oilfields, is already getting emotional.

Above) The Wangmobile, the Bakery Van, and Hank's personal limo on the Suffolk flatlands, and (*below*) the Wangfords going nowhere but always searching for the perfect loaf.

I'm standing in for Hank here in the doorway of the wagon, still with Susie and Roy, and new members of the band, Clancy di Angelo and, sitting, Kirby Cane – the Commander – our powerhouse drummer. Hank, meanwhile, is drunk in a beach hut. Dobbin does not sing with the band.

more under Frank's influence and spending most of his time in his company. And less and less with Maria. He was so busy listening to Frank's plans for the future that he didn't see he wasn't paying his wife the attention she demanded and deserved. She had become disillusioned with both Frank and Hank. She may well have been ingenuous but she certainly wasn't stupid. She suspected Frank's motives and thought he was self-centred and even dishonest. She had heard a few dark stories.

Hold on there, Doc! You were doing real fine, real sensitive up till then. Stories are stories and there's such a thing as libel.
> Yes, but I'm just telling what Hank told me *she* felt. I'm not agreeing with it. It's only the truth, remember? *We Talk Turkey*, right?

Sure, sure, We Talk Turkey, gobble, gobble, gobble-de-gook. I know, I know. But do we need all that stuff about Mexico and my work with the import-export business? Surely you don't always trust everything Hank tells you? He's a sick man, for Chrissakes, who thinks he's a *Singing Doctor*.
> What's the problem, Colonel? You've got nothing to hide.

Er ... well, no ... That's true ... Sure. Right, Erm ... yes, right. That's just fine. You're doing fine. Carry on.

Maria was a fiery and emotional woman and was getting no tender loving care from her new husband. As Hank became more and more distant she felt she could no longer reach him and started to look around for some loving. She needed a little warmth in the icy winter of their marriage. She got distracted by the quiet bassplayer Chico, who also happened to be her second cousin. They fell in love.

But Hank was blind and saw nothing.

At this time Frank got a job-lot of waiters' jackets and the seeds of the last straws were sown. The guys agreed to wear the jackets, but when they got them, they found that Frank had sewn a teacloth over the forearm of the left sleeve. He thought it would look good to see the teacloths swaying from the arms as the band moved round the stage. The Spanish Waiters did four gigs like this but in the end it was just too Miguel Mouse for them. They couldn't cope. They didn't want to cope. They didn't respect Frank any more so they just packed it in.

At the same time Pepito had some bad news for Hank. He told him that Maria couldn't take any more and had run away with Chico.

Hank was shattered. He had come into town, formed a band, got married, got a manager and then lost everything, all in just under a year. Everything gone. Everything except the manager.

He was most bitter about losing his wife and blamed Frank for it. But as Frank pointed out, the *wife wasn't in the contract*. Only Hank. *100 per cent Hank*. When he realized he couldn't actually leave Frank or he'd be sued, Hank ran away down to Oregon for a while and wrote some songs. It was springtime now and should be good in the woods.

CHICO

How long have you been going out with Chico?
How long have you been slipping round on me?
How long before I knew
That you were gone and I was blue
Ay ay ay, eres ermosa mi Marie.

The night I held you tight in the Paso Doble,
And whispered Dulce Nadas in your ear,
I never saw a sign
That you had someone on your mind
While we danced beneath the stars that shone so clear.

I thought that you were mine and mine for ever
I thought your cousin Chico was my friend
I never saw the glances
That you threw him while we danced
I thought our love was safe from other men.

And then one day Pepito took me drinking
To tell me he had something on his mind
That you had married Chico
And had split to Puerto Rico
Speak to me and tell me why I was so blind.

How long have you been going out with Chico?
How long have you been slipping round on me?
How long before I knew
That you were gone and I was blue
Ay ay ay, eres ermosa mi Marie.

Hank Wangford © Chappell/$incere $ongs

Like Cures Like

I got back to London in spring '72, a lot later than I expected. After leaving Saskatchewan I had spent time in and around Vancouver and San Francisco, Arizona and Texas. When I finally got back and contacted people I should have written to a year before, I could feel the resentment. I couldn't really resent the resentment as it was my fault for making promises I knew I couldn't keep. Even so, Miss Magendie certainly *did* give me an Arctic blast down the phone.

Musette Magendie, an extraordinarily fragile name for a woman of such military bearing, was the companion of Doctor Margery Blackie. Doctor Blackie is still the greatest doctor and healer I've been lucky enough to know. She was the Queen's homeopathic doctor and the Dean of the Faculty of Homeopathy. At the Faculty she was an inspirational teacher, and her Drug Pictures were legendary. Let me explain about Drug Pictures.

Homeopathic treatment is finding the right remedy which most closely resembles the patient. Each remedy, whether it is a snake venom, a mineral, a healing herb or a poisonous plant, produces a picture of symptoms, of characteristics, in any person who takes it or is exposed to it whether suddenly or long term. As this symptom picture is built up from many cases, it becomes like a person, a person of a particular type. So, from accounts of the symptoms in poisonings, from experiments where researchers take the drugs and note the symptoms and from various historical accounts detailed pictures of the effects of each substance are compiled. Why gather these symptom pictures? Because they lead to the essential homeopathic principle, called the Law of Similars, which says that Like Cures Like.

This traditional principle, always part of medicine, was redefined and developed by Samuel Hahnemann, the founder of homeopathy in the eighteenth century. Thus symptoms caused by a substance in a healthy person *will be cured if they appear as the result of a disease process and are treated by giving that same substance.* Arsenic is a perfect example; when it's given as a medicine or a poison it produces characteristic symptoms. It can give a watery, painless diarrhoea and attacks of asthma-like bronchospasm. More commonly the person becomes icy cold but has a desperate need for fresh air. But the overriding symptom is the *Fear of Death.* In accounts of classic chronic poisonings, the wife popping small doses into the old man's pudding, the victim gets increasingly cold and clammy and has *an overwhelming fear that he is being poisoned and is about to die.*

Thus, homeopathically, the asthmatic who lies there placidly wheezing through a severe attack is very different from the one who, running with cold sweat, clammy and frozen, rushes to open the window to gulp in cold air, terrified that he is dying. And these two people will need *different treatments.* If like cures like, then the freezing and fearful asthmatic, panicking and terrified of dying, will be cured by minute doses of Arsenic. The minute doses are important along with the Law of Similars, for the other theory of homeopathy is that the more dilute a remedy is, the more potent it is.

The theory of potentization is that every time a drug solution is diluted – 1 in 10 or 1 in 100 – and *succussed,* or shaken and banged fiercely, the poisonous properties of the drug are decreased and the curative powers increased. This, not surprisingly, has always been scorned by the medical establishment. Homeopathically, the most potent remedies are those which have been diluted beyond the point where a single molecule of the original drug is present. Orthodoxy has always taken this as confirmation that homeopathy is completely bonkers, and if it ever seems to work it can only do so on some derisory placebo or psychosomatic level. As the years go by, however, there is increasing evidence that, disconcertingly, potentization works.

With Doctor Blackie, the drug pictures *were* real people, alive and crystal clear. She herself shone with enthusiasm, and was like a piece of phosphorus dropped on to water, fizzing and boiling and bubbling as it twists and dances its way across the surface. She was a little woman with a classic grey bun who moved very fast, almost jerkily, like a wee bird whose eyes shone with an artless love of life. A born healer.

She was entirely practical and was devoid of pretension and snobbery, such simple faults for many great maestros. Her skills were to heal people and to teach others to heal people. No messing around, no rationalization, nothing intellectual, just *how to recognize people and their types and how to heal them.*

I sat in with her at her surgery for a long time before I went to Canada. It was a delightful anachronism, another world from another time. She would sparkle away by the crackling fire in her old drawing-room and her patients would be visibly healed. She asked practical, and homeopathic, questions like:

'Is your head sweaty?'

'Do you dislike stuffy rooms?'

'Do you like sweet or sour things?'

'Do you like sympathy?'

'Are you affected by thunderstorms?'

She'd never delve deep psychologically. She didn't need to. The closest she'd get would be 'Do you like your mother looking after you?'

'Get some Ignatia, Dr Hutt, a small bottle,' she'd say in front of the patient then, glancing over. '*I think it'll do Miss Lyall a great deal of good.*' Sparkle, sparkle. If she were Groucho Marx, her eyebrows would be dancing across her forehead. It's not hard to see that I loved her dearly. It didn't bother me in the least that I never met the Queen or that when minor Royalty came round to her consulting rooms in Thurloe Place, I'd be sent below stairs with the servants. I understood. I wouldn't have cared if they'd put me in a cupboard. It was the hair to the shoulders that did it. They thought the Royals wouldn't be ready for the Hippie Doctor. Quite right, though if I'd put my hair in a bun too I'd probably have got away with it. Still, Blackie and I got on very well together. She gave me the *Materia Medica*, a homeopathic reference book, that had belonged to Sir John Weir, the previous Royal homeopathic physician who had been King George VI's attendant. It was Sir John who had wangled homeopathy on to the National Health at its inception in 1948. But Miss Magendie was much more of a snob than Blackie, and her lifetime service in the Scout Movement wasn't likely to make her warm to someone as unScoutlike as myself. She had always been a mite suspicious of me from the time we first met.

So I wasn't really surprised when on my return to London a couple of years later I got the big freeze from Musette. There had been talk of my joining Blackie's practice on a more definite basis and I'd only got myself to blame for blowing it by turning up too late. The lure of the road had been too strong.

It was the one foolishness of that time away, not coming back when I said I would. I was sad for it, too, although deep down I knew I'd never have been particularly happy tending to the unwell well-to-do.

Sunny Side
☆
of the Street

Another doctor, who had a Harley Street practice, gave me a roasting rather than a freeze-out. He was Dr Lionel X, a bit of a wide boy, like a few of the lads up there. Along with a minimal general practice he ran a slimming clinic. At Doctor X's clinic you'd get a quick bit of medicking, a quick check of weight, and very quick pulse and blood-pressure checks. Then you'd be given some speed, maybe by injection, plenty of vitamins and diuretics, some meagre dietary guidance and Bob's your uncle! You're thinner!

It's brilliant, it's magic and it's so simple. Mind you, it made you a bit touchy, a little edgy, not too popular with your friends and colleagues. Sometimes you might think that everyone else was extremely upset and uptight, especially with you. You'd often feel like tearing people's noses from their faces, but you'd certainly stay thin. I don't think that X was one of the injections-through-the-tights brigade, but that did go on in the whacky world of pin-stripe private medicine. So Doc X had a lot of model girls on his books and as they didn't want to be on the pill with the risk of water retention, many of them turned to the coil. So he turned to me.

'Listen, Sam, you could make lots of money, more than you'll know what to do with. We could do really well together. They all need coils, or advice about that sort of thing. I sort out their figures and you sort out their fannies. We'll clean up.' It sounded totally OK ethically to me. I couldn't fault it, figures and fannies, hmm, Hippocratic enough I guess . . . but I said that right now I was packing in my private practice and was off to Canada and the States and would be back in three months.

When I got back the following year I signed on the dole and wondered about getting some part-time work doing clinics at the Family Planning Association to keep myself alive while I went on playing music. Finally I got round to calling up the good Doc.

'Hi, Lionel, how're you doing?'

'What the fuck do you mean how am I doing? How do you think I'm doing? I've been sitting here on my arse working my bollocks off and you've been having a great time poncing around America. Fucking all right for you, you tosspot, you've been OK . . .'

'Yeah, but,' it sounded like I had a crossed line. It was as if I'd called up a doctor and got some hooligan *Sun* reader who'd been denied his Page Three for the last year.

'Yeah but, yeah but,' he snarled. 'Don't give me that crap, you prat. You said you'd be back last year and I've had to look after all these cunts myself. Birds all want to be as skinny as a rake, I can do that for them, but you said you'd help me out and stick coils up their fannies.'

'No, mate, I didn't say that at all. I said I might be able to help them out with contraceptive advice, but that I was off to the States. No promises, remember.'

'Oh fuck off, you bleeding wanker, don't be so fucking po-faced about it. You were going to stick bits of plastic up their cunts and make lots of money.'

'Now, come on, Lionel, for Christ's sake, leave it out, will you? Shut your face and give your arse a chance.' This was getting more like a couple of dockers than doctors and I was beginning to get into the feel of it.

'Do me a favour, shithead, and save me the holier than fucking thou. I offered you the fucking chance to make more dosh than you could think of and you piss all over me.' He was really roaring by now. 'Fuck me, you ponce off to America to play your fucking stupid music and leave me here like a spare prick at a wedding to deal with all these moaning women wanting coils or caps or what the fuck, I don't know. So what am I to do? Send them to some dodgy third rate Wimpole Street gyno who doesn't know whether to stick the coil in their ears or up their arses?'

'Look, mate, that's nothing to do with me, that's your responsibility.'

'Oh, fuck my old tits green. Ha! You can stick your responsibility up your arse. You tosser, what the fuck do you know about it? I've got hundreds of anorexic dolly birds who need a coil shoved in—'

'Listen, shut up willya? Can you hear yourself?' This was getting ridiculous. By now I was listening to this sewage with the morbid fascination of a toddler in an abattoir. It was like a boil bursting down my telephone.

'Oh, sorry, I beg your pardon, excuse me. A coil perfectly inserted by the skilled and sensitive hands of Dr Hutt the eminent wanker . . .' and he started screaming again, 'so they can fuck their fucking rich Jewish schmutter business boyfriends in the front of the Ferrari and not get fucking pregnant.'

This was not a happy man.

'Listen. I told you. You could be fucking rolling in it. I mean, do you want to go on wanking around or do you want to make fucking money or not?'

What could I say? For this man The Edge was a thing of the past.

'Well, put like that, mate, I don't think I do. Thanks for the offer and have a nice day.'

The great thing about real life is you never have to exaggerate.

☆ ★ ☆

Telling this story, of course, in no way means that I am implying that all private West End doctors are woman-hating, scatological, mercenary perverts. Far from it. There are many admirable and honourable practitioners amongst the trash down The Street. And in terms of Greed before All, politically speaking the Good Doctor X was simply an early pre-Thatcherite, a voice crying in the wilderness, a pragmatic revolutionary. And if I'd ever challenge his integrity he'd look very solemn, the nearest thing to sincere he could get to, and say,

'But I won't treat Arabs.'

Just like that. Like I've got my pride, there's certain things I would draw the line at. Ethical. Well ethical. And I remember quite a few of the West End doctors who were raking in embarrassing amounts of money would say that,

'I won't treat Arabs.'

For treating Arabs could only be for the money, and silly amounts too. Bags with ten thousand on the desk. Whatever. The amount was unimportant. Health was important. Even to Arabs. I couldn't understand the complacently virtuous expression these doctors would assume when they had this spurious attack of scruples. It seemed to me to be a monstrous mixture of class-ridden snobbery and good old English racism. But what do I know, eh?

The trouble is, I simply have a problem with medicine and money. It's not that I'm the only honourable medic left on this sceptic isle, it's just that I still cling to the rapidly eroding notion that medicine should be free. One of the prime functions of a benevolent society is to provide **free medical care for everyone, and the decimating of medical services in** the Eighties has been a disaster and a disgrace. When money comes in, medicine gets somehow confused. In an overall sense, I can't see one for the other. It must be to do with the linking of money to *disease* and not to health. *How's business? Fine, doing fine, a lot of gall-bladder, heart and kidney trouble around at the moment. Oh, and a fair bit of piles.*

It's just a tad like being a vulture. Business is fine, they're dropping like flies. One of the problems is that it is far more profitable to *treat* established disease than to *prevent* it.

Illness is a growth industry. A nice little earner, it is far more lucrative than preventative medicine. The only hope is to tie money with health. You pay me for keeping you healthy. Giving advice, checking you out, looking after you. If you get sick, you stop paying me until I get you well again. I know it sounds like what the Colonel calls Hippieshit and I know it's not original. The Chinese were doing it thousands of years ago.

In the end, the nearest I got to Harley Strasse was an original Harley Street street sign, which had been ripped off by a chapter of American Hell's Angels on their first visit to Britain in the Sixties. It has the old-fashioned lettering from the quaint Borough of St Marylebone days before it was rationalized into the City of Westminster. It's still on my wall.

Listen, son, you keep slipping dangerously back into the Sixties. All that stuff is supposed to be for Volume II.

Yes, Colonel, I know, but I'm only giving a taster and not giving it all away.

***But you mustn't give anything away.* You know how I hate that phrase. Don't liquidate your assets.**

But I'm not, Colonel. I've only done a sketch of Doctor Blackie and there's a lot more about her and other home-opaths that I'm keeping for the next volume.

Ha! If there *is* another volume. After that filth you had in that so-called conversation it's almost certain we won't get this published in the States.

Times have changed, Colonel. People can cope with realistic language these days.

Realistic my ass. And another thing, worse than the language, is all that shit about homopaths. You seem to be promoting homopaths and saying it's a good thing to be. Now that's pretty damn irresponsible these days, what with Aids around an' all. You're even saying that you're one and I know for a fact that you go out with girls.

Jesus, Colonel, it's hom*e*opath, not homopath. It's a special kind of medicine.

Well, it sounds pretty unhealthy to me. Homo-, homeo-, I've told you before, just *keep it clean*. And keep it up to date, OK?

Whatever you say, Colonel, whatever you say.

The Family That
☆
Plans Together
☆
Stands Together

Everything seemed to be pointing towards Family Planning. There were alternatives, but I'd just blown my homeopathic chances for a while and I didn't fancy dealing in old rope down Harley Street. I'd always liked the idea of preventative medicine and of looking after women. I had already done a Family Planning course a year before I left England for Canada, and my favourite part of medicine when I was a student way back deep in the heart of Volume II was Obstetrics. Or, I should say, Midwifery.

When I came back from the States in spring '72 I was more interested in music than medicine, so I needed something part time. For a while I was out of work, which is not too difficult for me. I've never been a workaholic. Everyone I contacted was slagging me off. All the avenues were closing in front of me, so while I looked around for work and somewhere to live I registered on the dole.

Being a doctor, I was put on the Executive Register. I told them I was able-bodied and ready to do any medical work except general practice or hospital work. This puzzled the Social Security staff because they didn't think there could be any other form of the healing arts so I muttered words like Community Services at them. After about six weeks of checking in and signing on they started to get worried.

'Look, Dr Hutt,' the SS person asked, eyebrows knitting up an outsize Social Security jumper, 'it's a bit difficult to get any posts for you, you know, that are not in, well, general practice or, erm, you know, in hospital, that sort of thing.'

He looked genuinely worried, and as a doctor I was naturally concerned. I could see an anxiety attack brewing. I asked solicitously if there was anything I could do to help.

'Well, I don't know, doctor. I suppose if you are, you know, actually fit to work, I can't see why you can't, well, work in hospital or general practice ... But maybe ... you're ... not fit ... to work?' *A Brainwave.* 'Maybe you could possibly get me something like a sick note? That'd make everything very much easier.' Sure, I said, I'd see what I could do. I'd sort it out and see them next week.

A week later I brought a letter to the SS on my own Dr Sam Hutt headed notepaper. It said

> To whom it may concern:
> Dear Sir,
>
> ### re: Dr Sam Hutt
>
> This is to certify that I have recently under-taken a thorough medical examination of Dr Hutt and find him to be suffering from acute schizophrenia.
> I hope this is of help.
> Yours faithfully,
>
> Dr Sam Hutt, M.A., M.B., B.Chir.

You'll have to imagine the signature.

And the effect. It was a triumph of the Emperor's New Medical Certificate. The SS person leaned over and took the letter and glanced through it lazily.

'Oh, thanks,' he said, tucking the letter into my folder, 'that'll do nicely.'

☆ ★ ☆

Three days later I got a job with the Family Planning Association. Sixteen years later I'm still with the same Clinic. Must have been love at first sight.

When I first joined the FPA it was largely a haven for married or retired lady doctors to make a little something on the side. Far from being a serious speciality, Family Planning at that time was still con-signed spiritually to the Women's Institute side of life out in the Suburbs of Real Medicine. This was before Family Planning became known as Contraception, part of Women's Health Care or more recently and portentously, *Sexual Medicine*.

Nevertheless, even at that time, the FPA had a feel of women for women, albeit with its roots in Suffrage rather than Women's Lib. And in amongst the jobsworths and pin-money part timers there were people intensely involved in the true liberation of women from the shackles of their own special illnesses, of their contraception or even at times of their sexual subservience. There were many doctors and nurses there who had a refreshing lack of coyness about sexuality. Which was good because that's exactly what the clinics were dealing with.

If this all makes the early Seventies in the FPA seem like a haven of sense in sensuality then I'm painting an overly rosy picture. A lot of clinics provided routine and soulless fitting of caps, checking of coils, taking of smears or prescribing of pills. Some could be frightening, especially to women who were already anxious, embarrassed, confused or even ashamed. A lot of the nurses acted like surrogate mums reproaching their errant naughty daughters, but almost as many were jolly, no-nonsense women who obviously enjoyed doing rude things at home with the old man and didn't mind anybody else doing the same. Overall there was a kind of bustling *bonhomie*, a let's-all-pull-together Voluntary Services sort of feel. There was somehow in the air, the feeling of the post-war Forties, roll up the sleeves, tie a scarf on the head, no nonsense, get on with the job. A bit do-goody, perhaps, but what the hell, as long as good was being done.

For my first five years at the Clinic there was a figurehead, a director, who was of course male. The odd thing was that the post of Medical Director appeared at that time to be the preserve of retiring ex-Service doctors, an Air Vice-Marshal and a Lieutenant General. The first director, by contrast, had been a woman whose speciality was contraception and infertility. So it seemed like backsliding to start taking these Old Soldiers and putting them out to an autumnal pasture in the luxuriant if somewhat menopausal meadows of the FPA. I always felt there was a pungent symbolism in recruiting a retiring member of the Armed Forces to organize women's contraception. A Military Operation, perhaps?

I suppose to have chosen to retire into Family Planning at least indicates some sort of free-thinking liberal. Maybe not radical, but at least liberal enough to accept that people do fiddle with each other. Even outside marriage. And by some conservative standards that in itself was pretty liberal. Anyway, our two old soldiers were perfectly nice men who in their clinical practice were kind and did not despise women the way some gynaecologists can do. It just took us back in time. There was a touch of *noblesse oblige*, and they both made me think of General Booth of the Salvation Army.

87

It was almost as if the Sixties hadn't happened.

☆ ★ ☆

The Os is the opening, or mouth of the womb. The gynaecologist with the best name in the business, though I suspect he made it up, is a Dutch consultant called *Willi van Os.*

☆ ★ ☆

The classic contraceptive coil is the one that was invented for men. A small plastic umbrella was inserted up the urethra, up the penis, and guided – under local anaesthetic of course, we don't want our boys to worry – into the body of the prostate gland. Ukrainian farmers, remember? The umbrella was opened out and the device lodged in the little gland. It was an astonishing 98 per cent effective. It caused a little pain now and then during intercourse, occasional bleeding and once in a while the man couldn't get an erection, but it was nothing to worry about.

It was nothing to worry about in any case, for it never actually happened but I think about it when I'm in the Clinic and constantly reminded of some of the things women have to go through. Even if it had existed beyond the wild imagination of the feminist magazine that invented it, no man would ever tolerate the slightest possibility of those side-effects. Which is what the magazine was pointing out. Every day I'm doctoring, doing something as routine as using a speculum I wonder how many men would come regularly to a clinic and have a metal duck's bill shoved up their bottoms once a year to have a prostatic smear taken? I'd be out of a job.

Women put up with an awful lot and an awful lot of what they have to put up with is to do with men. They often tolerate far more than they should, especially in their health care.

Many doctors don't talk to women enough. It happens with men patients too, but women get the real sharp end of the stick. It's to do with *hysteria*. Women, we are told, are hysterical. This means they complain at the slightest pain and magnify, if not imagine, everything. It springs from the Greek word for womb, *hysteros*, and so has an even greater depth of meaning in gynaecological complaints. Women as hysterical creatures is a commonly held view in society as much as by doctors or nurses. Is it surprising that women can have this view of their own sex as much as men can? Not really, since it is reinforced especially in Britain by the Stiff Upper Lip. The need to appear unperturbed. But most medical or surgical procedures *are* fairly perturbing. And in the end it's better to show your fears than to bottle them up.

The fact of the matter is that it is *men*, not women, who are hysterical, who complain more, who cry louder, *who put up with less.* But because men are seen to be stronger, they are assumed to have *Real Pain*. So they are treated far more solicitously than women. Studies show that in hospital, when men complain of pain, they are prescribed more analgesics, and their pain is taken more seriously than women's.

So it isn't surprising that for a commonly painful experience in many women's lives, the fitting of a coil, few are offered anaesthetic. For some women a coil fitting does not hurt. For a great number it is painful; for some it is the worst pain they have ever felt. But some doctors refuse to accept this. Everything is obscured by the *hysteros*. The scenario is simple. The doctor is fitting the coil and the woman is crying. The doctor thinks: *I am a good doctor, caring and skilful. Good doctors do not cause pain. Why is this woman crying? Ah, because she is hysterical.* The game is lost. This patient is lost. Her confidence is shattered. The doctor can no longer treat her. *When a doctor calls a woman hysterical it usually means he doesn't like her.*

Doctors like this have come to me in the past and said with an air of feigned surprise, 'You give local anaesthetic for your fittings?' and then, with a thinly veiled smirk, 'you mean, your coil fittings *still hurt*?'

Yes, sometimes they do. I fit coils gently and skilfully and it can still hurt. But the implication is there for all to see. I am either a fool who is still cack-handed after all these years of practice or I pay far too much attention to whingeing women. Either way I am a wally.

☆ ★ ☆

I was once training a doctor, a bit of a hooray Henry with a public-school crinkle haircut, who confided that Family Planning was a last ditch attempt before he left Medicine to go into Law. Coming out of a consulting room he nudged me and whispered, man to man, into my ear. 'Funny creatures, women.'

Time stood still until I could gather myself up to urge him to investigate the Bar more fully.

☆ ★ ☆

Womb pain is always somehow imagined. There is no sexist attitude to teeth because we all have them. Or at least started out with them. So we are all offered injections if our teeth are to be drilled. Why not for fitting coils? Too indulgent? Too time consuming? Nonsense. A well-fitted coil is liable to work better, more efficiently and more comfortably, and is more likely to be well placed if the womb is not going through spasms, or the womb's cervix, its neck, going through shock.

One old gyno's tale is that the cervix *feels no pain*. Some do and some don't, but tell that to a woman as you clip a pair of forceps on to her cervix. Generally if a woman has babies, her cervix becomes less sensitive. Generally but not universally. I had a letter from a woman in

Scotland who said that a coil fitting hurt her *more than having a baby*, so when no one believed her and refused to give her an 'unnecessary' anaesthetic, *she had a fourth baby rather than have another coil fitted*. If we are told something that doesn't fit into our specialist view of things, *we simply don't believe it*.

This is not to say that anaesthetic is always needed. There are women who have no pain, there are women who have pain which is sharp but short and tolerable, and there are women who do not like the idea of a needle in the cervix. But, conservatively, at least fifty per cent have unpleasant and avoidable pain. Painkillers by mouth don't work. So, for true pain relief there is no way out, apart from hypnosis or acupuncture, but to offer local or even general anaesthetic, procedures that are completely normal in private practice but sneered at as wasteful, costly, indulgent and time consuming if the health care is free. It can only be assumed from this that private medicine itself is wasteful, costly, indulgent and time consuming.

One of the problems with medicine is that it is often doctor- and not patient-oriented. Doctors know some of the facts and some of the answers but are loath to share them with patients, wheeling out the old defensive, paranoid chestnut that a little knowledge is a dangerous thing. So the doctor diagnoses the illness, weighs up the chances and decides on the treatment usually without discussing it with the patient. The only discussion is likely to be about the treatment the doctor has decided the patient will have. Unless the patient is private and is paying, in which case they become a customer. And as we know, in an open market the customer is always right.

All this is much worse for women who get far less information and are far more patronized than men. It boils down to one thing: *if you are going to fall ill, be a man*. It's safer. That way you'll be told more, believed more and treated better.

It seems that the first two guiding principles of medicine, first do no harm and then relieve pain, are too often overlooked. As coils are potentially both harmful and painful, I know I should do everything I can to protect the people I see. *Iatrogenic* means doctor-induced, and there is an unacceptably high percentage of hospital admissions, often quoted at around fifteen per cent, for iatrogenic illnesses. Contraceptive measures can add to this with complaints like coronary thrombosis, pelvic infection, perforated uterus and various neurological compli-cations. That's not all but luckily most of these problems are rare and it is easy enough to avoid them with a little sensitivity and a lot of common sense. There is nothing clever about it. But then there is nothing especially clever about being a doctor.

The trouble with living in a commercial, let alone monetarist, world is that when money is a prime motivation its interaction with medicine has the potential to be extremely dubious. It is the same with the Arts. Money and commercial efficiency are necessary and are not of themselves evil. It is only when the commercial principle threatens to overcomes the artistic or the humanitarian that creative or ethical problems arise.

In my view for drug companies to call themselves ethical is an inspirational irony, a piece of Sincere Speak that shouldn't be lost on the Colonel. As the satirist Tom Lehrer explained when he decided to retire from performing after Henry Kissinger was awarded the Nobel peace prize, *Life has started imitating Satire.*

Another view, however jaundiced, is that as a doctor I am the grocer, the retailer. Seen even more cynically, I am the dealer, the pusher. So the drug companies like me very much. They court me constantly and not just with piles of literature or free samples or desk tidys. They give me lunches and they sponsor conferences; they fly me to those conferences that are in far-off sunny climes. They finance clinical trials of their new product, all perfectly ethical and safe as they may well have already tried the drugs out on poorer people, on *foreigners, Third Worlders*, before we try them in this country. This *can* all be done with propriety and has to be seen to be so, for the medical profession and the manufacturers are walking an ethical knife edge.

Another observation is that *turnover* is important. However ethical the manufacturers, they are making *Product* for the medical world. And product must be *turned over*, whether it's drugs or whether it's high-tech. scanners.

Or whether it is coils.

Since the early Seventies, a second generation of coils has been marketed. The first generation were bigger and caused more pain and bleeding. The later coils were smaller, with a sleeve of copper wound on to them. The copper seemed to increase the contraceptive reaction of the womb to the foreign body and thus the coils could be physically smaller. They were potentially more comfortable, causing less pain and bleeding.

Not surprisingly, the idea for putting copper on coils came from . . . Chile! And the Chilean gynaecologist who did pioneering work had the exotic name of Jaime (pronounced Hymie) Zipper. Putting copper on inert plastic coils was a brilliant move from two points of view.

Apart from being smaller, it made the coils work better. There were still problems, though, especially in women who hadn't had children.

Commercially they were a godsend. Copper dissolves into solution and sets up the reaction of the womb lining. If it dissolves, it must wear away which it does, at different rates in different women, very gradually over several years. If it wears away, *it must be replaced*. The problem with the previous coils was that they were inert, they didn't wear out. Here at last, we have obsolescence.

So they had to be replaced. How often? When do they wear out? At first, in the early to mid-Seventies, they were changed every two years. Soon, coils came in that would not need changing for three years. Then new, improved models came in which did not need changing for five years. Yet there is very scanty unconvincing evidence to suggest that a decreasing copper concentration goes hand in hand with an increasing pregnancy rate. So why change at five years? It was still maintained with minimal evidence, rather in the style of a Nostradamus prophecy, that there would be a *late pregnancy rise* after five years. It appeared, however, very difficult for the drug companies to organize a long enough survey with enough women in to show this fabulous late rise in pregnancy. *Well, you know how it is, women always going off to have babies and that sort of thing. Difficult to organize. Funny creatures, women.*

Naturally it didn't seem to be such a problem for the World Health Organization or the Population Council. So they did a six-year survey of women using a new model with extra copper on it. And there is *no late rise even after six years.* Another Mexican survey of this model showed no late rise in rates of pregnancy or pelvic infection *after ten years.*

The license date is fixed in agreement with the DHSS. The companies will argue that it is the DHSS who will not increase the time on grounds of insufficient evidence. In reality it is that there is insufficient evidence that changing the coil decreases the risk of pregnancy or pelvic infection. In fact the reverse is the truth, as we shall see. I am certainly not suggesting any complicity or corruption between the DHSS and the drug manufacturers. It is simply that someone is dragging his feet, and in Thatcher's Britain where efficiency is all and the National Health Service is being carved up, money and health are being cruelly wasted. If coils are still in use in ten years time, we certainly won't have to change any of them. And that's nothing to do with Nostradamus.

Why such a fuss? Should it be surprising that there may be a strong commercial consideration in the routine replacement of coils? Well, not surprising, but unacceptable. It not only represents a vast amount of unnecessary suffering for women, but also involves a scandalous waste of money on an enormous scale.

What is all this, Doc? You're beginning to sound like some kind of pinko socialite or something. How can money be wasted if merchandise is being sold? Why are you knocking the drug companies so hard?

Well, they're supposed to have a responsibility to humanity...

Bullshit. Drug companies aren't charities. Responsibility never paid the rent. If they don't sell, they go out of business, there's no medicine for you to prescribe, and then where'd you be, huh?

Yes, but...

What you goddam Commie doctors don't realize is that marketing means selling, whether it's coils or cars. And if anybody gets better through using the companies' products, that's what makes it ethical.

But Colonel...

No buts, Doc. Less knocking of the drug companies. We're thinking of forming one ourselves – \$incere Pharma-\$euticals where we cure all – so lay off, will ya? Keep the politics out. Talk about the women. That'll sell books.

When women talk to me in the clinic, most who have coils think they need to be changed because if they get too old they get infected, that pelvic infection is commoner if you keep a coil in for too long. As if it goes mouldy. Nothing to do with a risk of pregnancy. Yet the change-over, the point of taking one out and putting a new one in, *directly increases the risk of pregnancy, uterine infection, expulsion of the coil and pelvic infection*, for the months following the changeover. By introducing instruments into the womb, however careful I am, there is always the possibility of introducing bacteria and thus infection. Our Hippocratic Oath says *First Do No Harm*. Of course, a changeover can be done without all this happening, but the statistics are clear and incontrovertible. Too many times at the clinic I have had to counsel a woman for a termination, or treat her for an infection, just after she has had a changeover of a coil that had previously given her no problem at all. *FIRST DO NO HARM.*

So we wait for any convincing evidence for routinely changing a coil in a woman who does not have to put up with any unpleasant side-effects, who is happy, who has regular checks and smears and wishes to continue with the coil as her method of contraception. *If it ain't broke, don't fix it.* I am happy to see healthy women and even happier to leave them alone. Some women cannot escape heavy and painful periods, and the terrible shadow of pelvic inflammatory disease still hangs over the use of the coil. But used carefully, coils can be for many a release from the systemic effects of the pill. *The best medicine ever is no medicine at all.* And after all the advances we are still happiest for people who are using the older barrier methods.

What of the men's pill? Is this all a male conspiracy to enslave women? Well, as a man it would be invidious of me to say it wasn't. That's what I would say, though, and I'd give reasons, sincerely felt, why the hormonal control of spermatogenesis, a continuous process of sperm formation, is fraught with difficulties such as the production of mutant sperms. It is physiologically easier to prevent the release of already-formed eggs, eggs which are present when the woman is born. I don't feel the balance of women's exploitation would be redressed by similarly exploiting men, but rather to look forward to a hormone-free future for everyone. But I would be bound to say all this as I am a man and, worse still, supposedly an expert. And experts are dangerous people, not to be trusted.

In my darker moments, and some of those are when I have had to do a particularly traumatic coil fitting for someone, I wonder whether deep down I want to hurt women, to enslave them with hormones or dangerous bits of plastic in their wombs, rather than to liberate them into a life of carefree sexuality. A wolf in sheep's clothing? my subconscious asks. A raging mysogynist posing as Mr Nice Guy? In the end I don't think I am, but it's OK to have these self-doubts. Now and then, at least, they help to keep perspective. It's not difficult to feel worried when a woman is shaken to her core with cramps shortly after she has come to prevent an unwanted pregnancy.

And there still seem to be some punitive procedures. Painful coil fittings. Painful coil changes. Large, tight fitting caps with excessive amounts of cream. Cold metal speculums. Taking the decision whether to have an abortion or not out of a woman's hands. Yet all these can be solved; coils can be fitted painlessly, caps can be comfortable, less cream is just as effective (but, alas, no cream is not), speculums can be warmed, and a woman, albeit not within the letter of the law, can decide for herself whether she can become a mother.

If this all seems very black, it must be said that I love my work in the world of family-gynaecology-planning-psycho-sex-women's-health-sexual-medicine-care. That's exactly why I don't let Hank relish going round being called The Singing Gynaecologist. He sings. I do the doctoring. Sometimes I sing, but he never doctors.

I enjoy doctoring. I respect a lot of the people I work with at the Clinic and I respect the confidence of the people I see and it is because of this confidence, and because most gynaecological jokes are by definition sexist, that I have very little medical sense of humour. I can't abuse the privilege of being trusted with secrets, maybe spoken for the first time. Women have already had too much abuse in their lives, let alone their health care, without some smart-alec doctor making wisecracks about them.

Very Sincere, Doc, I like your style. Very Sincere. And I think there's a large female audience out there for the book, so keep it up. Don't hold back.

Thanks, Colonel, thanks *a lot*. Just when we needed to hear from you . . . Finally, in the middle eighties, several drug companies in the United States made the commercial rather than medical decision to drop the manufacture of coils. They were disturbed by the increasing number of women who claimed they had been damaged by coils, organizing themselves to do battle.

Against a background of crisis in the Liability industry, and in the face of increasing litigation and decreasing profits and the insurance companies' refusal to provide cover at a reasonable rate, the drug companies decided to pull out of the coil market.

Anyway, in this funny old world of ours, if something cannot be insured, it ceases to exist.

No pay no play, as the Colonel would say.

Heathfield '72

I had never really wanted an upwardly mobile career in medicine so it was hardly surprising that I blew any chances I might have had when I came back from the States. It was just as well as I had a head full of songs and all my ambitions were musical. Right then I just wanted to play with other musicians, to try out songs, to keep writing. I wasn't settled anywhere and was dossing around for a while. I was having to doss wherever I could and keep moving because no one would let me stay for long, recognizing the very real danger that before anyone noticed I might put down roots, take the place over, put a studio in the bedroom and set up my consulting rooms in the lounge. Doors all over London were closing gently but firmly in my face. Though I was back from the States I was still out on the road.

I was still signing on the dole when I first started going down to Heathfield in Sussex at weekends to stay with my friend Mike Storey. Mike was a singer and pianist who was struggling through the jungle of the music business, playing and singing with different bands and trying to carve out something for himself. He'd just been in a band called The Last Supper. He was renting a little cottage by a little lane in the rock-star green belt on the outskirts of London. Our resident rock star in the large house next door down the lane was Mitch Mitchell, the drummer from the Jimi Hendrix Experience. The only contact we had with him then was when we were pottering down the lane in our Morris Minors, he would race out of the house and cut us up in his Range Rover. Apart from Mitch there was a small community of musos who did actually go round and visit each other and play together. It got very stoned sometimes, slipping easily into non-stop E minor to A funky jamming, perpetual motion in music, but what the hell, playing together nonetheless.

To be fair, the interminable E-minor solos were more common in Formentera (near Ibiza), a stop on the fabled Hippie Trail. Parties on Formentera, especially Full Moon parties, quickly degenerated into the Night of a Thousand Drums, bongos and congas all doing the simplest of drone beats, *DDOOMM boom boom boom, DDOOMM boom boom boom*, throbbing relentlessly like the natives-are-restless jungle drums in an old B movie. All attempts to play *songs* with chord sequences were futile. Guitarists inevitably got heaved back on to the one chord, the perpetual E-minor jam.

In Sussex, Storey and I enjoyed doing a lot of two-part harmony; he'd been at a cathedral school and sung in the choir as a kid and became my Consultant Harmonist. He found harmonies very easily and showed me how to find the good ones. We were both writing separately but I had more completed songs at the time. The songs? Well, the total immersion in Country music out on the Canadian Prairies had pushed me towards much simpler songs. I also knew that I wanted to sing, to perform Country music. Canada had made me ambitious. But musically the songs had a way to go yet. The early Seventies were actually still the Sixties, so although the songs were moving into a Country idiom, they were still firmly rooted in the sensitive singer–songwriter tradition. *Songs to sing to Girls*. Sensitive songs about being alone and suffering, missing you late at night, yearning for the touch of your skin and all the time hurting a lot, hurting . . . but . . . with . . . a . . . hurt that could be eased by the right woman. Feeling inside you, all that sort of stuff.

I wrote an awful lot of crap for a very long time before I could get down to writing half-way decent songs. I had to wade through a huge backlog of shite of my own making before I started to write clearly from the heart. Anyway, there was still a lot of Free Love around then, and we believed wholeheartedly in it. And why not? No one knew the difference between sexy and sexist in those days.

> Colonel Frank wants me to let you all know that there's going to be plenty of Free Love all the way through Volume II in case you were disappointed in the lack of sex here in Volume III.

Sometimes Storey set up his Hohner electric piano out in the garden and we'd sing a bit, probably hoping that somebody over in Mitch's garden might hear and leap over the garden hedge and offer us a recording contract.

Over the next few years we played together in various different forms, but down in Heathfield we joined with some other guys and formed the makings of the first band since I came back from the States. Mick Cox had been the lead guitarist with Eire Apparent, a fancied Irish band who'd had connections with Hendrix. He played a lovely fluid, Bluesy guitar with a lot of bottleneck, a languid, sinuous style somewhere between Ry Cooder and J. J. Cale. Fitted nicely with Storey's lyrical piano playing. And all held up well with Charlie Harrison on bass and Steve Chapman on drums. Charlie had the tightest trousers of us all and the smallest bottom.

We became Stanley and his Famous Negroes but didn't get very far down the gig circuit, or even very far out of Heathfield. Through the mists, and there are a few of them around at this time, it seems we did no more than a couple of parties and some pubs. We *may* have done a pop festival but we may not, and the mists are so thick it's hard to be certain. I keep meeting people who say they saw the Famous Negroes playing and we were great, but inevitably *they* can't remember where they saw us any more than we can. What seems to be sure is that we *did* do some public gigs somewhere . . . Certainly the Negroes came down to Dorset and we played in Stourpaine a year later when I had a house there.

Whatever happened, we enjoyed the music so much that I remember the Famous Negroes with an especial fondness. Mick Cox did a solo album and recorded a couple of my songs. One was 'Hanging on to Columbia', a pretty song about Vancouver but with lines about totem poles and hidey holes to slip inside that would make it ideologically unacceptable today. The other was 'Prairie Hotel', a song with a long solo section in – you've guessed it – E minor and A. Mick went on to play with Van Morrison. Steve and Charlie went off to California and became the rhythm section for Poco, a classic if West Coast country-rock band. Steve went on to play with Al 'Year of the Cat' Stewart and Charlie with Rod 'No Relation' Stewart. Mike Storey stayed in England, changed his name to Michael and became a serious composer, and is now well known for his fine film and television work.

So the alumni of the Negroes all acquitted themselves well in the outside world. S & the F N were even inserted into one of those classic family trees of the West Coast groups, one of the Byrds, Buffalo Springfield, Crosby, Stills, Nash and Young, and Poco. And all from a few days and nights sitting around getting swacked, sniggering – sorry, snegroeing – and playing a tune or two. After Steve and Charlie left for America, Mick, Mike and I did a good few gigs over the next couple of years, but no longer as the Famous Negroes, who slipped quickly and gratefully into legend.

Mick Cox and I did one monster gig together. Those in the business will realize the poignancy of the billing. We were playing two acoustic guitars and singing sensitive Country songs to a reeling retching crowd of . . . HAWKWIND fans! We were supporting Hawkwind at Watford Town Hall. And Hawkwind fans are like the drug-culture, heavy-metal equivalent of British Country fans. They went to hear Hawkwind *and no one else*. Not Sabbath or Zeppelin. Just Hawkwind. Psychedelic modal heavy metal. So on our acoustic guitars we didn't have much of a chance. The crowd lurched about yelling 'Hawkwind' and 'Fuckoffyoucunt' solidly for the whole forty minutes we stayed on stage.

Against all the odds we did manage to stay on stage for the full forty minutes. I just told them I was staying, and that was their tough shit. We also managed because the crowd could do nothing at all to get us off apart from shouting at us and threatening us with their beer glasses. They were completely out of it on beer and downers, the traditional Hawkwind fans' mixture. Beer and barbiturates make a very rubber-legged combination, so there was a lot of falling over, quite often just as someone was trying to throw a glass at us. As they raised their arms back above their heads they were thrown off balance by the weight of the glass and fell backwards. Luckily there was usually another Hawkwind fan on the floor behind them to break their fall.

Mike Storey stayed in Heathfield for the rest of '72, and I went on working at the Clinic. Mike and I went on playing and singing together and dreaming of our Album covers. Through him I met Rob Hamer again.

Smack, Smack,
☆
Naughty Boy

Rob Hamer was a famous bass player who I had known when I was the Rock Doc before I fled the fleshpots of London for the rape fields of Canada. He had recently stopped playing with a massively popular supergroup and was spending a lot of time at his out of town mansion with his head in a bucket of heroin. I was fond of Rob who was a bit of a softie, but with a voracious appetite for the smack. He really loved it. He had a taste for Country music, too, at least something I could share with him. I played him some Merle Haggard songs and some of my own from the time in the States and Canada. He liked the new songs and asked whether I'd thought about recording. I said I had, but no one had offered anything. So he said he thought he'd like to work with me on an album which we'd put out on his label. I wasn't going to argue.

So I went down to his house a few times to work out what tracks we'd do. Storey and I went down for two nights to record some songs on Rob's new tape deck, but Rob hadn't quite figured out how it worked. They were two long, long nights. At least it was summer and dawn came early. Mike and I sat waiting and playing, singing songs, getting ready to record, while Rob, hunched over his new tape deck in the corner of the huge room like a wee dormouse, tried to get the gismo to work. He fiddled, hit the machines, cursed and spat and snorted all night long, but nothing happened. He seemed small and fragile as he sat right over the other side of the huge room, crouched in the green half-light of his whirring high-tech. toys.

'Sorry, mate, I couldn't quite get it going right,' he said as the morning sun came pouring in through the windows. 'We'll try again soon, yeah? I'll have it sussed by then.'

We were still able to work out a lot of the songs we wanted to do, but didn't do the home demos. Then I had a brainstorm on Midsummer Day. I called Rob up to say if we were doing a Country album, there was one obvious person we should have to co-produce it. Gram Parsons.

It turned out Rob knew Gram too so he called him to see if he was free, and he was. When Gram came over he was carrying a copy of 'We Go Together', George Jones's and Tammy Wynette's latest album. Gram had already met his Tammy, a young unknown called Emmylou Harris, and had George and Tammy firmly in his sights as role models for a solo album he was planning. I was knocked out that he had taken time out to come over. But that's when Mister Horse rode roughshod over all our plans.

I've always been an outsider when heroin has come around. It is a very exclusive drug, warm to the junkie cradled in its arms and icy cold to anyone outside. It excludes and dissolves away the world. This time, when I went down to Rob's home, he and Gram would be huddled, dissipated, in a corner and I was definitely not included. I could feel the dark shadow of smack blighting the air. Unsmiling. Blots out laughter. I was not in the club, so I was left behind. That, of course, is how I saw it, but the smack could have been incidental. I'm ready to blame it for anything, I hate it so much. It is very likely that Gram wanted to get on with his own project and that mine was a diversion that was not diverting enough. Whatever the cause, I came up against an impenetrable barrier that appeared out of nowhere and all the plans just disintegrated. Just like that.

Gram went back to the States and made his first solo album. Some of the finest duet singing ever with Emmylou. Storey and I went our separate ways for a while. I settled into Bina Gardens, my basement flat in London, and Mike went off to Formentera to write songs and sing to girls. Later he came back and found himself the doss of a lifetime with a sunny room in a film producer's house up in leafy Hampstead.

A year or so later I caught up with Hamer and he agreed to come and do some demos we were planning. By this time things were looking up. I was writing more songs and playing with Mike Storey again. I don't know whether we had been heard playing with Hamer in a room somewhere or seen playing a folk-club gig like the Troubadour but somehow we'd got a manager. Let's call him Ronnie Coleman. He said he'd like me to be his solo act. He'd already got his group, a fine Scots band called the Average White Band. He'd been given sackloads of money by Great Western Express, an offshoot of Harlech TV, to set up a pop-management company.

So I said yes, I would be his singer–songwriter, and Mike was my band and backing vocalist. I asked Ronnie for a retainer *and he gave us one.* I got a couple of hundred quid, and a fiver for my mate . . . no, but I got one hundred for Mike, definitely less than I got myself . . . Still it was a good touch and we both couldn't believe our luck. Ronnie was good natured about it all, but could afford to be with the unnumbered wheel-barrowloads of dosh he had coming into his office all the time. I didn't know then that he supported Chelsea, but I'd probably have accepted the retainers anyway. Just another showbiz compromise. Just a few more scruples to deal with.

But Coleman wasn't that bad at all for a Chelsea supporter. And there we were with a manager who had us on retainers the like of which don't exist these days. We were rocking, even if it was on shifting sands. So the next move was the demo record and then flog it round the record companies. This is where we met Rob Hamer again and he said he'd like to do the tracks with us. I had been seeing a bit of Pete Townshend who had been encouraging about some of the songs. Storey and I had been down in Pete's little home studio, with Townshend playing bass. Real lead-guitarist's bass, too, lots of notes. He said he'd come and play guitar on the demos too. I was getting nervous.

On the day, I was still nervous. In fact I was scared shitless, but I was enjoying it. The session was in Olympic Studios, in the big studio. This is the studio that The Stones and The Who recorded in and their engineer and producer, Glyn Johns, was engineering the demo session . . . Hell, I had watched The Who recording bits of Tommy in this same room . . . And then, god help us, it looked like we were going to get Jim Keltner on drums. The King. I began to panic. At the last moment, almost to my relief, Keltner couldn't make it. It would probably have been too much for me, too many stars around. In fact I was delighted to have Mike Kellie of Spooky Tooth, an Only One in later life, on drums.

It was still mad, though, doing this demo in Olympic, with Glyn Johns engineering, Townsend on guitar, Hamer on bass and Kellie on drums. Storey on piano was a pillar of strength. He was my lifeline to the musos and, in spite of it all being a bit overwhelming, the session went very well. The tapes sounded quite big and guitarry, quite muscley without being heavy. Pete had a really clean volume pedal which meant he could do swells like a pedal steel, and fake some Country sounds. He faked them really well, but I've always thought of him as one of the world's great bluffers in music. It's a real skill. Townshend like a lot of great guitarists has his own language which has its own feel, and it's the feel that is more important than the technical virtuosity. His style is simple without a lot of flashy runs up and down the fingerboard.

We did 'Northern Comfort', about Canadian Prairie moonshine, and 'When will Jenny get a Man Again'. We recorded it all live, the only way to record, but something I've managed all too rarely since. There are always a million reasons why when we record we must do the bass and drums first, and then build up the other instruments and voices layer by layer over the rhythm track. Or so I am told. But this time it was live and went smoothly and easily. After the first two numbers, Rob went off to the bathroom to stick his head in the bucket.

The next song was to be a moody one, about friends who had got fucked up on heroin. Most particularly about Joe, my quarter brother – I come from a complex family – who died of an overdose. So when Rob came back spaced from the lavvy I had to tell him the next song was called 'Smack, Smack, Naughty Boy'. He nodded and clambered back up on to the high stool he always played on. Half-way through the first runthrough of the song Rob, who had been playing hunched over his bass nodding intently, straightened up and leaned back a little as we moved into the pokier middle eight. Slowly and gracefully his high stool tilted back and with his back staying in a straight line with the stool he fell backwards in a perfect arc on to the studio floor. Lying there in freeze frame on the floor, still attached to the stool, staring straight up at the ceiling, Rob kept on playing without a pause or even a flicker.

Always the true professional, *he never felt a thing*.

☆ ★ ☆

Neither did we for a while. It was like delayed shock. The whole thing had been so grandiose that the dust never really settled. We could be forgiven for thinking, playing with all these stars in this holiest of all places, that *we had made it*. Hell, our manager had spent twelve hundred pounds on a four-track demo session. A lot of money in 1974. We're talking unlimited budget here. We were *Rocking*! Ha! Poor fools! We'd hardly even stepped on the great tightrope, let alone got to the other end.

Coleman did his job well and soon came back with an offer. Warner Brothers had come up with a recording contract, a deal to produce two singles, with further options if we had any success. Instead of jumping at it, we thought the offer was derisory. This was still singer–songwriter time, remember. Any performer worth his salt wasn't doing singles, but was putting out *albums, proper artistic statements*. An Artist needs enough room to make a real statement.

We're talking *Integrity* here. And if Warner Brothers don't understand that, we'll just find a record company who will.

But right there, Doc, that's where you first went wrong, mixing up integrity and sincerity.

What do you mean, Colonel?

Well, the whole key to the music business – any business – is seeing the huge difference between Integrity and Sincerity. Most record companies *are* extremely sincere, but I don't know one with any integrity . . .

Thank you, Colonel.

You're welcome, son. Like to help out when we can.

Anyway, we *had* to make an album.

Singles just weren't *sensitive* enough.

So what did I do? Thought about it, stood and looked at the letter with the offer from Warner's with Storey down in the Bina Gardens' basement, *and got depressed*.

We decided we were worth more than that and told Warner's to piss off. Which is exactly what they did. So did Ronnie Coleman, figuring quite reasonably that if I wanted to go round staring gift horses firmly in the mouth, I was welcome.

But not on his time.

When God Comes
☆
and
☆
Gathers His Jewels

In the early summer of 1973, about the same time I was getting ready for the Great Olympic Demo recording, my father fell ill. Out of the blue, his legs began to feel weak. In a very short time he couldn't walk properly. He had held court in the basement kitchen all his life, but now his legs wouldn't carry him up the stairs to his study. So he slept in the back bedroom behind the kitchen and pottered between the two. X-rays of his back showed his spine was like spaghetti, riddled with secondary deposits. After a lifetime of smoking the big C had caught up with him.

He had been a newspaperman, journalist, typographer and historian all his life and after several years had just finished work on the manuscript of his last book, a history of newspaper design. When the tests came back from hospital and the extent of the spread of the disease was discovered, it was astonishing that he had gone on symptom-free for so long, that the illness had held off until he had finished his book. But a disintegrating body is often held together by force of spirit. On the other hand, if you don't want to live, you probably won't.

So we all prepared ourselves for the worst, the Death by Cancer, the wasting away, watching the poor man being trapped inside the shrivelling body, behind the hollow face and sunken eyes. Doctors call it cachexia. The very word sounds like a death rattle, but it didn't happen.

Although he couldn't get about so well, he still had lots to do. Most importantly, he needed to organize the index to the book, and he had to go to hospital for his radiotherapy and for regular check-ups. I became very distressed because he didn't want to acknowledge that he had cancer, he didn't want to talk about it. I resented my stepmother when she told me not to tell him the diagnosis. As far as he was concerned, he was having deep cobalt therapy to harden his spine. My stepmother was being very protective and would not let me discuss the details of his illness with him. I argued with her but she prevailed. This ban was made all the more poignant by her being a nursing sister and me a doctor.

It's a common enough thing for boys to feel closer to their mothers than their fathers, especially if their fathers take a spiritual back seat to a dominant mother. I was no different from many and my emotional communication with my father had been fairly minimal for many years. But whatever kind of old sod he had been, I still loved him for his humour, his erudition and his charm. This seemed like the last chance we'd get and so I felt frustrated that a final opportunity for a new and cathartic openness was being squandered. I just wanted to make my peace I suppose, but sadly for me, the chance never really came.

The old man had always had a funny habit of not looking you in the eye when he talked with you. A lot of people have it but most look away or bring their upper lids down, closing their eyes, when they point their face at someone. Dad had his own endearing way of avoiding total eye contact. He would talk to you face to face, but would be staring intensely past your head at a spot three inches to the side of your right ear. Many times when we talked I would playfully hop over six inches to my right but as soon as I had plonked myself bang in the centre of his vision, his pale watery eyes would flick away again past the side of my head. In the past, on times when I did try to get through to him I often got so wound up that I'd start to shout and bluster at him, dodging from side to side trying to hit his line of vision. And right then, so suddenly a sick man, with his back collapsing, the last thing he needed was me blustering at him.

In the end my stepmother was probably right. He was an intelligent man and must have known what deep cobalt therapy was for, but didn't want to talk about it. Many people are like that and it's their right not to know, as long as those who do want to know get told the truth. I still found it very hard to pretend to his face that he wasn't dying, that things were getting better. We all wove a fabric of lies with him. If it was a charade, it was one that he clearly wanted to play. But this was all academic for in not much more than a couple of months he was gone.

He had slowed down a lot, so he pottered quietly through the final

Hank, deeply confused by his own publicity as a singing
gynaecologist, seems to think that this street sign will bring
him closer to the hippocratic fountainhead.

Even the Bertolt Brecht Award for Street Cred. Pre Designer stubble cannot salve the hurt of being falsely accused of crimes against $incerity. I was standing in for Hank while he was unable to stand himself, *never* trying to oust him. 'I only meant to borrow not to steal . . .'

Right: Inside, looking out, alone with my thoughts, I wonder, would Hank have done it this way? (Students of safe sex in cowboy hats will be reassured to see the Stetson Condom, ready for any emergency.)

Paying the price. On remand, waiting for my hearing, I try to make it up to Hank in a hurriedly arranged gig in the prison.

When you're really $incere, justice can't but triumph. My name cleared, I speed off to find Hank and help him with his battle with the bottle.

But instead of finding him drunk, I found Hank practising his $incere eyebrows with the grand master, George Hamilton IV. Disappointingly, he can only manage a semi-George, and the King himself seems to be resting.

summer months, organizing the index for the book, peering at Wimbledon on the TV, and speaking to old friends. He didn't really get sicker through this time but just older. The expected rapid deterioration didn't materialize.

His last week was spent tidying up. He'd done the index and was now writing letters. He wrote four letters to important friends and colleagues. Harold Evans, *The Sunday Times* editor, came over to tell him that *The Changing Newspaper* was brilliant and was going to be the definitive history. At the end of the week, I think it was late on Friday morning, he wrote a last letter to a final friend. Still perfectly clear, he said he felt a bit tired and went next door to bed. A short while later he sat up.

'I can't think any more,' he called out and, painlessly, his heart stopped.

☆ ★ ☆

When I first heard the news over the phone, I laughed out loud with relief. I was delighted for him that he had gone with so little suffering, but saddened for myself at leaving so many things unsaid. So what's new? That's the way of the world, and right then it was my problem. For his funeral he wanted to be cremated with the Trumpet Voluntary playing and, like the good old Communist he was, he wanted his ashes to be tossed over Karl Marx's grave in Highgate Cemetary.

When we got to the cemetery with our box of ashes, and probed our way through the wild thickets of God's Acre On The Hill, we found a group of East German and Czech tourists in front of Marx's grave paying homage and taking pictures. The monument has an imposing black bust of The Man sitting on top of a high plinth. He looks very hairy, with his great mane, his huge dynastic beard and bushy, beetling eyebrows. We were a little self-conscious, with all the East European Comrades there with their cameras, so we crept round the back, opened the box and started to sprinkle the ashes round the base of the monument.

After a minute or two of this we looked at each other and knew. This was *not* the way to go. No excuses.

So we rushed round to the front to start sprinkling there, Comrades or no Comrades. I wanted the old boy to go all the way, so I grabbed handfuls of his ashes and jumped up at the bust of Karl, flinging them right into his face. There were ashes everywhere. One of my nieces found flakes of her grandad floating in her hair. We laughed and cried and got very excited. And when we had done, and all the ashes had been flung, we stood there between Karl and the Comrades, and sang 'The Internationale.'

Arise ye starvelings from your slumbers,
Arise ye criminals of Want . . .

Trouble is, I never can remember any more of the verses. So I hmmed and na-naed my way through. Out of the bleary corner of my eye I could see some of the East Europeans were joining in. Impossible not to really, it would be like standing in church at Christmas and not singing 'Oh Come All Ye Faithful'. Ask Pavlov. When we finally got to the chorus of 'Then Comrades come rally, and the last fight let us face', I looked up at the great looming head.

Then I saw them.

Hanging from Karl's eyebrows, draped over his eyes like silver veils glinting in the sharp daylight, were some fine spiders' webs. And hanging on the cobwebs, flickering and bobbing in the breeze, dancing like a dry snowstorm in front of the great man's eyes, were my dad's ashes. The tears welled up and I started to choke again.

If Communists go to heaven, I thought, the old man's there already.

☆ ★ ☆

Eighteen months later I had a startlingly vivid dream, one of those that is too real to be just a dream. One where when you wake up you feel like you've just fallen asleep. The old chestnut where you're not quite sure whether you're a butterfly or a man, dreaming or waking. That sort of thing. In this dream my dad and I sat there talking about everything in the way you can only do in dreams. We said all the things we'd been holding back for too long. He made me laugh, but then he was always good at that, always told a good story. He told me his side of the family story for the first time, of how he felt through the break-up, of how the Communist Party got involved in our family politics. I told him how I had been dreading and dreaming of the break-up for five years, and then of the huge relief I had felt when my parents told me it was all over. Though it had been a long time coming, the final straw was when the the Russians steamed into Hungary and crushed the rebellion late in 1956. It took Stalin's tanks to liberate my family.

I told him 1956 was the year of rock 'n' roll. He reminded me it was the year of Suez. I told him 1956 was actually *1958*, that our memories were getting hazy. He said he didn't care. I asked him how he could have stayed in the Communist Party after the disillusionment of Hungary. My mother's faith had been shaken and she had drifted away from the Party. He talked of counter revolutionaries and said that if you were a Stalinist there was no problem at all. I remembered the picture of Uncle Joe, smiling and benevolent, hanging on the kitchen wall like the Pope in a Catholic parlour.

We talked about my first love affair, a Camden Town Romeo and a Gant's Hill Juliet, she a pretty Jewish piano student and me her skinny Goy boy. An eleven-mile walk back home after the last train from Hainault had gone on a Saturday night. Ain't love grand. We talked about his last love affair, with my stepmother, his third wife, and why I had never exactly welcomed her with open arms. A bit of a mother's boy, see, very loyal. Like Elvis, or Hank Williams. Or Genghis Khan.

So we talked and we talked until we were done. Then I woke up. And any of the regrets I'd had over the previous year and a half about not confronting him with Basic Truths in his lifetime just disappeared. They were no longer there.

I had made my peace, even if it was only a dream.

☆ ★ ☆

The old man had gone up to Cambridge to read History in 1919, the year after the Great War finished and two years after the Russian Revolution started. He did what any thinking person, let alone student, would do in the early 1920s and joined the British Communist Party. Later he was the Chief Sub Editor, the designer, of the Party's newspaper, the *Daily Worker*, for more than a quarter of a century. He was also active in the National Union of Journalists, the NUJ, and was the Editor of the NUJ organ *The Journalist* for the same time he was at the *Worker*. He stayed Editor all through the Cold War, Reds-under-the-Beds years, in the face of a lot of reactionary pressure.

Of course his typography, his newspaper design and layout, had nothing to do with politics. He left the *Daily Worker* when it changed its name to the *Morning Star*, far too revisionist a move for the old boy. He did a lot of freelance consultation and helped redesign different news-papers all over the world. He felt his proudest moment was when he was commissioned to redesign the *Jewish Chronicle*. He wanted to put a little brass plaque on the door

G. ALLEN HUTT
Typography Strictly Kosher
Licensed by the Beth Din

He was an only child of middle-class parents. Two generations before him had worked at Macmillan's in Cambridge. Paper and printing were in the blood. With his politics you might say he was middle-class with working-class pretensions.

My mother, a Mackinlay, came from Glasgow, from Govan, and was also an only child but from a working-class family. When the two of them met she was a strikingly good-looking young teacher. Her father had been a linotype operator, more printing, but died when she was very young. Her mother, my Nana, worked in a shirt and pyjama factory. Being famous in Glasgow for my height as a kid, I had plenty of pairs of oversized flannelette pyjamas made by Nana and her friends. Mum's grandfather, my great-grandfather, was the infamous Rover Mackinlay, who was a boilermaker and who walked out on his wife Mary McElhaney and their children. It was said that when Rover roved, when he walked out, Mary, who was a washerwoman, turned her face to the wall and grieved for ever.

But when mum and dad met, she was a teacher, part of a profession and therefore middle class. They shared political views. And she looked like a film star. What was an old Commie to do?

Doc, we've told you about the politics. We're not planning to sell behind the Iron Curtain, so why all this Commie crap?

I — . . .

I don't wanna hear. You've been getting away with murder. What's all this bullshit about the Marx Brothers being Bolshie?

That was Kar . .

I don't wanna hear, right. **Forget the politics and get back to Hank. And Country Music.**

OK then, Colonel. Just one more though . . .

☆ ★ ☆

I carry the legacy of my father's bronchitis, though when I was a cigarette smoker and was hacking away well, I followed Lenny Bruce's classic advice and claimed it was TB.

He always said bronchitis sounded poor and Jewish and with a deep phlegm filled rasp would croak 'I got bron-chytis' in a thick New York accent. Much better, much more charismatic and cool, he said, after a heavy coughing fit, to purr from deep down in the throat, eyes heavy lidded and half closed.

'I got TB, baby'.

No-Show Jones

When I first heard that George Jones and Tammy Wynette were headlining the Easter 1974 Wembley C & W festival I couldn't believe it. It was too good to be true. Ever since Gram Parsons had introduced me to George I could listen to no other male C & W singer; it took me half a decade to be able to see past George and start to hear the voices of Merle, The Louvins, Webb, Ernest or Willie. It was the full ten years before I heard Lefty Frizzell, George's finest musical forebear aside from Hank Williams. But we're jumping ahead, and I had met Hank Wangford before I even heard Lefty.

In '72, when Gram came over to see about helping produce the Country album with Rob Hamer and me, he was carrying the new album from George Jones and Tammy Wynette, called We Go Together. It featured a dynamite photo on the cover, my first taste of what I found later Tammy maintained was George's impeccable dress sense. She talked of it in her engagingly candid autobiography *Stand By Your Man*. What she probably means is his ability to co-ordinate clothes far better than he can co-ordinate his life. I guess it's finding the right shade of azure belt to match the socks which are toning in to the sky-blue easy-on-the-go *lee*sure suit he's wearing over a matching cerulean polo neck.

But on the We Go Together album cover, George goes beyond mere mix 'n' match of his own outfit. He and Tammy are sitting hand in hand on the porch of what looks like their house. He is wearing a light-coloured sports jacket and pants. More remarkably, she is wearing a crimson crinoline dress, Scarlet O'Hara style and *George is wearing matching red, patent-leather cowboy boots*. When I first tore the album from Gram's hand, I was speechless. It seemed like I had always loved his voice and now, with the red patents enhancing and embellishing his lovely wife's dress, hell, I even fancied his footwear. Boots are still in style for manly footwear, yes sir!

If my memory serves me well, George may even have had a matching crimson shirt, making the co-ordination total. Any confusion I may have had was cleared a few years later when Hank explained that in Country and Western music, as in life itself, *It's better to have bad taste than to taste bad*. This guiding principle has carried me through many dark moments in the intervening years.

I was mesmerized by George and Tammy's voices. Tammy's was simpler, not the heavenly instrument that George's was, but had such a silvery clarity and in particular such a distinctive *cry* that I could Accept No Substitute. George's was astonishing, weaving and swooping like Ray Charles but with an urgency and tension all his own. A lot of his melismatic dives and turns are like fellow Texan Lefty Frizzell. Not surprisingly, Lefty's ferocious battles with the bottle were close to George's. Close, but not in the same legendary class, for George is in the Superbowl of boozers; he's Olympic standard, Gold medallist many times over. He can pack twenty years of drinking into one two-week bender. And Lefty's drinking career was cut short prematurely in 1975 when his brain burst at the tragically young age of forty-seven.

What makes George's voice unique is not just the raw yearning and not just the heartaches but the painful restraint of his fiercely clenched jaw. He sings like an angel whose wings have been clamped. All the painful fluidity of his phrasing comes through a jaw held so tight it might as well have been wired together surgically to prevent him from eating solid food. It is the perfect Country vehicle. It has passion and repression. It has pain and tension. It has the Blues and the guilt. It is free and it is inhibited like a wounded bird.

Melisma is the twisting and stretching of a note, of a syllable within a word. It is the creating of an improvised and ornate melody within the melody of any song. It is a spontaneous ornamentation directly in touch with the singer's emotions. It is not thought out. It is heart, not head. It is integral to Black Gospel and Soul music, to the Blues, to Country and to a lot of Ethnic music.

It is universal.

My two enduring loves in music have been harmony and melisma. My first live melismatic thrill was hearing Ray Charles in person in an unlikely English cinema when I was seventeen. There was that voice just as I knew it on record, shouting, torn, heartfelt and vulnerable. I didn't know then that the Fifties were dark times for Ray. He looked helpless as he was led on stage, stooped and stumbling, his arms wound round his chest as if he was stopping himself from falling apart. These were the days when there were rumours of Ray being forced on stage at gunpoint by heavy management hoods. Only rumours perhaps, but it *is* Showbiz. Don'tcha just love it?

My love of harmony had already come from the Everly Brothers long before I realized they had been nurtured in the heart and soul of Country tradition. Ol' Uncle Ray had boldly fused Gospel and Blues, sacred and secular, to the howls of rage of the committed purists, and laid all his emotions out with his raw and soulful phrasing. Ten years later I fell in love with the similarly breathtaking twists and turns of Indian classical music. Nazakat and Salamat Ali Khan made my heart pound just as Ray had done and as George Jones would soon after when I stumbled over him in the early Seventies. To me George has always been the Ray Charles of Country music.

To sing good Country is the same as to sing good Rock 'n' Roll. You have to be in touch with God *and* the Devil and the battle is right there in every song.

A lot of this was racing through my mind on Easter Monday in 1974 as I sat trying to be calm in the great concrete barn of Wembley Arena. It was the interval before the final set. I looked round and saw people still coming in. The place looked fuller than it had been earlier, but wasn't completely sold out. Now it was just a matter of minutes before George and Tammy were due on. I was so excited my brain felt like it was an egg boiling and bubbling round inside my skull.

It was one of those classic times when you can feel your heart pounding inside your chest, leaping into your throat and throbbing behind your eyes and you know that any minute that old heart is going to come bursting out of your ribcage. You're just waiting for the SSPLLATT!!! to give your secret away and let everyone know that you're not really a grown-up at all. It was OK because I could see that all the hard-core Country blockheads around me felt the same. There wouldn't be a dry stetson in the house.

I looked desperately down at the floor as I tugged at my scorpion bolo.

'It's going to be George and Tammy any minute.' I screamed a whisper through clenched teeth and waved my fists down at my old pair of pointed Tony Lamas. I didn't have any red, patent cowboy boots to honour Mr and Mrs Country Music, but the Lamas would have to do. I could still stamp my feet with pride.

As an avid winkle-picker fan since my teens I had fallen in love with the serious needle points of the Texan boots ever since I'd seen all the farmers in Saskatchewan wearing them. Unlike the Shitkicker style of boot, chisel-toed presumably to get more purchase on any offending cowpat, the toes of my Tony Lamas came to a vicious point that seemed to veto the structure of the normal human foot. Years before, I had paid no attention to my mother's earlier admonitions, for winkle-pickers were surely not sensible footwear, and had managed to crush my lateral arches with over-enthusiastic fashion consciousness. As a result, I couldn't believe that the Texan boots didn't similarly annihilate the feet. But strange to tell, they were far more comfortable than they looked like they deserved to be. They were called Roachcrushers and were reputedly designed, as well as enhancing the machismo of the manly foot, to deal with motel cockroaches cowering in the sanctuary of the corner. *SCRUNCHH!!* Gotcha!! No mercy!!

It was while I was shouting under my breath at my boots that the lights started to fade. I looked up and saw a spotlight starting to glow round a lone microphone in the middle of the stage as the house lights dimmed and engulfed us in a comforting darkness. I leaned forward expectantly as I saw a man dressed in a white suit step into the spotlight.

He stood for a moment in contemplation, his head bowed and his left arm bent, a black book in his hand. Silence.

'Friends,' the word rose shakily from somewhere deep inside as he began to look up at us. '*Friends, my name is Bill Anderson.*'

It's Whispering Bill, the fans whispered to each other and a patter of applause went rippling round the Great Barn, tempered with a nervous anticipation provoked by Bill's exorbitantly emotional tone. Why is he sounding so sincere? we all wondered anxiously. I knew already deep down in my Tony Lamas exactly what I didn't want to know. Something awful was going to happen. Or had already happened.

'*Friends, just a couple of days ago . . . my good friend . . . George Jones . . . told me on the plane comin' over here to your beautiful country, he told me how much he was lookin' forward . . . to singin' to his fans over here . . . erm . . . in . . . your . . . er . . . beautiful country.*'

Oh, Jesus Christ, he's not coming. Oh NO! It can't be, say it can't be. Please, we want to see George and Tammy, please, please, please . . . But alarm bells were going off in my head and I could feel the icy fingers of apprehension creeping round the auditorium. Nine thousand people start to hold their breath. Christ, what's going on? No, c'mon, now, surely George must be here, he must be, he can't have . . .

But Whispering Bill's tone was slow and dark, almost funereal and I could swear the black book he was holding so tightly and pressing to the folds of his white suit was the Bible. He hardly had to say any more. I could feel the worst hanging in the air like a shroud. His voice quavered with sincerity.

'*As we touched down here in London George leaned over and asked me if anything went wrong . . . would I take care of things? When I asked him what he meant by that he said he didn't really know . . . He said he wanted to meet and greet with you wonderful people here in Wembley so much . . . that he worried kind of . . . that sometimes when you want a thing so much, those are just the*

*times that something happens . . . He said that sometimes the Lord is telling us
we should not desire things so much . . . and sometimes Life just don't give us
exactly what we want . . . I tell you, I didn't understand everything he was
saying, but a little chill passed through me right then friends, and I was . . .
caused to shiver.'*

He stood silent for a long time while we all felt the little chill and
were caused to shiver. The spotlight dwindled gradually, focusing tight
around his upper body and face.

The black book was still there, over the heart.

*'At three o'clock this morning the telephone rang in our hotel . . . It was for
George Jones and was a call from Nashville, Tennessee . . . It was a call to tell
George that . . . his mother . . . had . . . passed on.'*

He was croaking now and the throb was pulling down to a
quivering whisper.

*'At that moment . . . George suddenly realized . . . that he had had a kind
of . . . premonition on the way over and knew that he had to go back immediately
to Nashville to join with his family . . . Tammy Wynette, his wife, knew that it
was her place to be by his side during his hour of need. So, with sadness troubling
their heavy, heavy hearts, George and Tammy flew back home just this morning.
George called me up before he left to ask me to talk with all his friends here. Do
you think they'll understand, Bill? he asked. Sure George, I told him, they're
British, we speak the same language and they all love you. Ain't that right,
friends?'*

Bill was much more forceful now. He was picking up speed and
was beginning to fly. The fans, prompted, gave a burst of applause
which sounded far less disconsolate than I expected.

*'You folks are so good. Thank you. Perhaps if you all feel the way I do for
George in his sadness and great loss . . . and the loss of . . . a mother is the . . .
greatest of all . . . Then perhaps if some of you friends and neighbours would like
to help George, you could write to him. I'm sure in my heart that if George
received your condolences they would help him in these dark times . . . And I can
feel the love coming from you, I can feel you people are like old friends . . . So do
please send your wishes and your postcards to George Jones, c/o Grand Ol'
Opry, Nashville, Tennessee and he'll appreciate it, I know he will.'*

Everyone was numbed. No one moved. No one breathed. My
heart had shrivelled up. Everything had stopped. We were stunned,
paralysed. We were putty in his hands.

It was then Whispering Bill came in with the masterstroke.

*'But there's something we can all do even before that . . . Something we can
do right now.'*

He was trembling visibly and seemed on the edge of sobbing. He
was really giving it the business now and was surely not holding back.

I was in shock and white with rage.

Something here was definitely not right.

'George is an intuitive sort of person. He should just be arriving in Nashville right now. If we here could all rise and perhaps stand for a minute's silence for George's mother's passing, why, I'm sure George will feel it in his heart at this very moment. And I'm sure that he will take great comfort from it . . . So if you folks would all like to rise . . . Thank you all so much.'

And, incredibly, 9,000 people stood up and observed a minute's silence for George Jones's mother. I was one of them.

'Thank you so much, so very very much. God bless you all, you are such fine people. I tell you—' he dabbed at his eyes *'—you . . . feel . . . just . . . like . . . family.'*

I was fuming but my rage was suppressed. I could hardly believe that I had stood there for a minute's silence. I just couldn't believe it. I was stunned that Whispering Bill had managed to turn 9,000 people from asking for their money back into 9,000 people observing a minute's silence for George's dear departed mother. I was as gutted as a retching parrot.

No hold it right there, Doc. You're getting a bit high and mighty there.

But, Colonel, how can you wait until the last moment before telling them that the star attraction isn't there? Why wait until the last moment?

Well, son, that's showbiz. Sometimes you've got to do things you don't like for the good of the show. The show must go on.

But that's not fair on the fans, Colonel.

Well, you're wrong, son. You see the fans have had a lot of excitement for their money . . .

Oh, come on, Colonel, that's . . .

Whoa, there son, I know you're upset. I can understand, but just take a moment and think about it. A lot of fans bought their tickets months ago and have had all that time getting wound up and excited about seeing George and Tammy. Genuine excitement, the real thing. Money can't buy that, and nobody was to know they weren't going to actually see them.

But Colonel, I can't believe you're saying all this. We paid to see George and Tammy, not just get excited . . .

Look, Doc, just calm down and listen. One day these good folks, who've paid their hard-earned money, are real happy and thrilled that they are about to see their heroes. That's a good feeling, you know, and something I wouldn't want to take away from them.

Yes, Colonel, I know. I had the same feeling. But this is

bullshit because the bottom line is we didn't see the people
we paid for.

**I'm coming to that. OK, they're going to be disappointed.
For a short while. But so is Mervyn, have you thought about
that? He wanted to see George and Tammy too. He was let
down too. But he asked Bill Anderson to talk to the people
and comfort them just as Tammy was having to comfort
George. So for the ordinary price of a ticket the fans witness,
no, *become part* of a unique, a *priceless* experience. At no
extra cost, Bill has drawn them into a very personal and
religious moment, almost getting in touch with the spirit of
George Jones' mother. That's got to be worth it, son. I mean
how often do you get invited to George Jones' mother's
funeral? Hell! I should think that would be one of the high
spots of any serious card carrying Country fan's life. Talk
about keep the faith! That'd be enough to give me the faith.**

That's all very well, Colonel, but we paid to see George and
not his mother's funeral.

**Yes, but if George isn't there, what do you do? Just give the
people their money back? Say you're sorry?**

Yes.

**NO. They'd be as disappointed as the promoter was. This
way they join George in his moment of grief. They have a
deeply moving and personal ceremony entirely free.**

It had been a day of Tragedy. George Jones' mother had died. George
was grieving. His mother had passed over to that radiant shore and we,
the punters, had been left high and dry.

Coincidentally, George was infamous for not turning up and later
he became known publicly as 'No-Show Jones'. When I finally caught
up with him live in Nashville twelve years later, he opened his set
self-mockingly with 'They call me No-Show Jones'. Years of disappearing off on week-long benders with ten seconds notice and missing gigs throughout the land have made George as legendary as Hank
Williams as he could be without dying in the back of his car. But when
you're as good as Hank or George the fans will forgive you almost
anything. You're part of their lives so it's like they're forgiving part of
themselves. It's a very close relationship. Country stars pay far greater
attention to their fans than Rock stars. I wish Country promoters did the
same.

Chief Shilo

But I couldn't keep away, and was always going back to the Country and Western Faculty of Wembley University for further studies. I became a regular, along with the gun toters from Billericay and my favourite Indian, the wonderful Chief Shilo from Forest Hill. Sounds quite Indian, Forest Hill, as long as you leave out the London, SE23.

Chief Shilo was a winner, always magnificently turned out in his finery; a real bone breastplate, an authentic full Chief's head-dress, buckskins and genuine Indian artefacts from various different tribes hanging all over him. He says he has always been drawn to the Indian culture and likes nothing better than to take you on a guided tour of his gear.

'Well, most of this is Cherokee, like,' he'd say, his slightly camp South London accent somewhere between Alf Garnett and Frankie Howerd. 'The breastplate and the head-dress are both Cherokee. The breastplate is made out of proper buffalo bone, like, and the head-dress is the real thing too, made out of Golden Eagle feathers. Had that fifteen years and it's still good as new. Just sponge the feathers down, and they come up lovely. Got it from the Queen Victoria reservation near Tulsa, Oklahoma. These here are my Navajo rings, real turquoise, got them from Gallup, New Mexico. And these are real grizzly-bear claws in this necklace. It's Sioux, got it from Wyoming. My buckskins I've made myself, like, but all to an authentic pattern. A mate of mine, Grey Eagle, who is a dentist in California, has helped me out with some things over the years. He married a girl from Manchester, and he's doing very well as it happens, got a yacht and a flash car and everything. I made these moccasins, too, and the design is from the Sioux.'

'Er indoors, his wife Little Elk, comes out with Shilo on a lot of his appearances. She dresses much more modestly, not the grand finery of the Chief but just a simple little buckskin dress, a headband and a single feather. And always with a fag dangling from the corner of her mouth as if it were an integral part of the costume, a kind of symbolic pipe of peace.

Apart from appearing at every WembleyFest since it started in 1968, Shilo does other Country jamborees, promotional shows and charity gigs. One day in the early Eighties Hank called him up to hire him for a couple of specials. On the phone, Shilo offered Hank a choice of two tepees, the small or the large. Hank, ever careful, went for the small.

'Do you need any Braves?'

'Braves?'

'Yeah, we've got a full tribe down here. We've even got a genuine Blackfoot with us.' Hank wobbled a bit at the thought of a whole tribe of Forest Hill part-Blackfoot Indians descending on the gig.

'Oh, I don't know, Shilo, they'd probably cost too much for us . . . How much is the tribe?'

And so the haggling went on. As Hank thought, the tribe was a bit over the top. Not a lot for a whole tribe, granted, but still out of the Wangfords' reach. The Chief was a hard-nosed negotiator, never gave anything away. The Colonel would approve. Hank used to call him Chief Shylock but loved him all the same. This time he plumped for just the Chief, Little Elk and the small tepee.

Playing the part to the hilt, Shilo and Little Elk arrived at the gig in their Cortina in full gear, feathers and all. The tepee was strapped to the roof rack and they had brought their Blackfoot braves free of charge anyway. Hank was stunned by the dedication.

On the night, they were magnificent. After some heart stopping moments as they struggled to erect the tepee on the slippery dance floor of the Notre Dame Hall hard by Leicester Square, all went smoothly. Shilo stood imperiously at the tepee while Wangford fans rocked, jived and cotton-eye Joe'd their way around him.

Later he dazzled everyone with a rain dance up on stage, the high spot of the show. Round and round he went, chanting, shuffling, bending, whooping and jumping with Little Elk, still with the fag in her mouth, just behind him. And Shilo got right into it. He was a man possessed. His eyes rolled up into his head and he was gone. There are not many people in this hard-boiled old world who are lucky enough to be doing something that they love with as much passion as the good Chief.

☆ ★ ☆

Maybe if the Country Music business were run with more of that kind of love and less cynical showbiz expediency it would appeal less to the lowest common denominator than it has done. It's as if everyone in the business, be it the managers, promoters or even the artistes themselves have decided what those outside Country music have always suspected, that it is just music for bozos.

For years, Nashville has been trying to tear out the hillbilly roots, to hide the shame of the poor white trash who gave birth to much of Country music. Even white liberals could not feel sympathy with this roots music in the same way they could the blues. They could lionize the poor black man and feel a comfortable guilt at his exploitation but still feel shame about the poor whites they perceived as rednecks, ignorant, fascist, sexist bigots. The trouble is that these despised bigots are the backbone of middle America.

And this feeling of derision, this same lack of respect for the audience was there at Wembley. Sure, most of the people in the huge Wembley warehouse were just ordinary folks. Sure, a lot of them liked some of the simple pleasures in life like dressing up as cowboys and Indian princesses and having mock shoot-outs. Sure, many were drawn to the soft, inoffensive, middle-of-the-road underbelly of the music, but so what? Everybody, even heavy metal or opera fans, have the right to listen to good or bad music. And who is to say that Jim Reeves is closer to the middle of the road, less sharp-edged or more anodyne than Ozzie Osbourne or Offenbach?

One year, the guest appearance at the WembleyFest of that well-known C & W performer Bobby Ewing of Dallas fame caused more bozo excitement than any of the bona fide Country stars. More fans rushed the stage dementedly and more automatic infra-red self-focusers flashed for Bobby than would even for their very own Tammy Wynette.

But amongst all that there have always been a goodly proportion of genuine Country music lovers at Wembley. These folks were rightly outraged when someone of the status of Merle Haggard was replaced once at the eleventh hour by the Osmond Brothers ('We've always loved Country music and used to sing it back home when we were kids'), who appeared to be climbing with a misguided opportunism on the sadly shrivelling bandwagon of mainstream Country music. Too little, too late. But hold on, now, which Osmonds are these? I can't see Donny . . . Where is Marie . . . or Little Jimmy? . . . Not at Wembley, that's for sure, where we were treated to Ray, Alan and other assorted Osmonds. It was would-be Las Vegas. Wembley regularly brings out, amongst some gems, the very worst in Country music.

It was often the Study Sessions between songs that captivated me at the C & W Faculty of Wembley University. There were always some redneck classics along with bullshit of mammoth proportions. Advanced professors of C & W like Freddie Hart or Boxcar Willie have pushed back the boundaries of sincerity over the last decade with some astonishing introductions and dedications.

But the basis of the fake sincerity is in the real thing. That's the difficult part about it, telling the two apart. Back home, a lot of the country folks *are* hospitable, polite, warm and welcoming, and a lot of Country singers do come from that background. What sounds to a British audience like an over-the-top hunk of hokum can often be surprisingly heartfelt.

When Freddie Hart says that if only he could stretch out into the dark, reach out into the audience and close his arms round the back of each and every one of the good people there and hold them and squeeze them close to him, then and only then would they understand how much he loves them all . . . he is artless enough to mean it, and mean it from the heart. But then he *is* Country Music's very own *Mr Sincerity*.

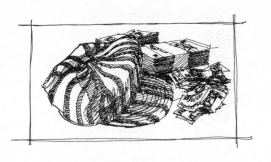

Boxcar
☆
and other Willies

Boxcar Willie, on the other hand, is
a different kettle of catfish. He says you can always tell the real thing.
He should know, not being exactly the real thing himself but rather a
genuine reproduction of a railway hobo. He has the battered old hat,
the battered old dungarees and jacket, the red bandanna and the battered old guitar. He is a supremely ordinary singer who became massive with the Country audience in Britain long before he had any
success at home in the States. He sings old train songs drearily but the
secret of his success is in the eerily evocative train-whistle sound that
he does, and the sincerity of his presentation. Unlike Freddie Hart,
though, his is not a natural but a sentient, a studied sincerity, $incerity
indeed.

'It's like being married to a person,' he explained gravely to me
once, giving me a tutorial in the rudiments of sincerity. 'If you don't
truly love that person, they will soon know about it. They can always
tell real quick – you can't hide it from them.' His pole-vaulting eyebrows hung motionless for a moment, floating across his forehead. 'It's
the same with any audience. It is like being married to them and they
can tell right off if you're being truly sincere . . . They know . . . they
can feel it . . .' I could tell he was being truly sincere. I knew. I could
feel it.

Professor Willie (call me *Box*) gave an astonishing, finely honed
demonstration of the state of modern sincerity in 1982. We might be

moving into Volume IV here, but I'm sure the Colonel will allow you just a little taster. It was during those dark, headily nationalistic days of Britain's South Atlantic conflict, the Falklands War.

After the backing band had been playing for a while, Box sneaked out of the side of the stage, hardly acknowledging the crowd or the applause. Head bowed, staring at his bootlaces, he walked slowly round and round the stage, holding his battered old guitar by the neck. He reached for his red bandanna and wiped his brow. Every now and then he looked up at the audience out in the great gloom, his shoulders shuddered in his battered old jacket and he looked down again. Obviously a Man Alone. An emotional man. A man whose trek round and round the stage seemed like his own personal stations of the cross. After a well-calculated eternity he came to the microphone and started singing.

Two songs later he said, slow and low.

'Friends, we weren't gonna say this but . . . well, we just have to share it with you all . . . You may have noticed that when we came out on stage, we were just walking around for a while. Couldn't start singin' . . . And it felt so emotional out here on the stage, all the love comin' over from you good folks . . . Every time we looked up and saw y'all it just kinda bowled us over. We looked out there and saw all those friendly faces, it felt . . . it felt . . . why, it felt *just like comin' home . . .*'

By now his voice was a deep rumbling growl as he nearly swallowed the mike. The audience was gasping. An ecstatic ripple, a shiver of delight. He had them by the throat, and wasn't going to let go yet. The good Professor Willie hadn't finished with them quite yet. The demonstration had only just begun.

He was going for Scholarship-level Sincerity.

'And friends, if you find yourselves standing on the edge . . . if you're on a tall, high cliff . . .' He was really preaching now. 'Right on the top of a great cliff, friends, looking down into the deep, black a-byss below . . . we want you to know . . . each and every one of you to know . . . that we'll be standin' right beside you

WHEN YOU BOMB THEM ARGENTINIANS!'

Well, hot dog! Hank and I sat there stunned, open-mouthed, our jaws dropped to the very ground as the arena exploded into a convulsive patriotic frenzy. It erupted like a great boil, I tell you, and Boxcar knew exactly how to burst it.

Yea, Boxcar, tell 'em how it is!

There, Doc, that's exactly how you and Hank should do it. That's the kind of politics you need in this book. Inspirational.

But, Colonel, that was what I couldn't— . . .

You see, your kind of politics are called *left*, right, because

you should have *left* them outside the door. Boxcar's are called *right*, because they're *Right*, right? And because they sell records, right?

Right, Colonel, right on.

Boxcar had tapped the darker side of sincerity at the Wembley Country Festival. Many others were far more benign, going for the heart rather than the throat:

'I thought the last audience we played to were fantastic, but they in no way prepared us for you folks. You're the best there ever could be.'

'It's always bin our life's ambition to play here at Wembley.' A good standard, always a winner.

'We'd like each and every one of you out there to feel as much at home as y'all are making us feel. Don't be shy – *there are no strangers here, only friends we don't recognize . . .*' Inspirational.

Conway Twitty was introduced once as '*The best friend a song ever had . . .*' No words . . .

☆ ★ ☆

Marty Robbins was always a straightahead, no-nonsense performer with a wonderful voice and massive charisma. Many times he charmed the Wembley audience with his hyped-up extrovert personality and delicious three-part close harmonies. The trio would sing with his tiny acoustic guitar, all grouped round a single microphone in the old-fashioned way. 'El Paso', the longest cowboy song in the world, was bliss.

One day he came bounding on to the stage at a hundred miles an hour, grinning from ear to ear, flinging his arms around and leaping about like a demented speedfreak.

'Hi, there, everybody,' he bellowed out to the crowd, 'HI THERE! Good to see y'all again! How're y'all doing?' He stood there, his arms outstretched, drinking in the rapturous applause and grinning wildly. He punched at the air a couple of times like a footballer who had just done an eight-yard run for a touchdown.

'Ha! I tell you, it's *good* to be back . . . You know, some people say I drink before I go on stage.'

He looked around the waiting faces of the faithful and I could see a twinkle glinting in his eye from fifty yards away.

'Nope,' he shouted triumphantly, 'IT'S DOPE!!'

Everyone applauded. It was the emperor's new clothes in reverse. No one heard a thing. The words went in ten thousand ears and out ten thousands others. Understandable, really, for what fans are ready to hear one of their heroes come right out and say that he was stoned out of his crust?

Selective deafness is crucial in certain areas of C & W. When you set the real lives of many Country stars against their images a bit of mental sweeping under the carpet is essential. No one can be that pure, that abstemious or that monogamous. Hell, it's the same with American politicians. Or even, God help us, with American TV evangelists.

Hank heard Marty loud and clear, though, and was mortified.

☆ ★ ☆

About this time I became a paid up member of the CTAS – the Conway Twitty Appreciation Society – organized by a Dave Gregory from his home in South London. Dave's name and address happen to be burnt into the remnants of my memory because he was also the editor of the CTAS quarterly fanzine, *Lonely Blue Boy News*. Apart from bringing me news of every live appearance of the Man of a Thousand Haircuts and a personal message from Conway, or at least from Dave Gregory, the best part of the *LBBN* was the letters column. Now I've always just been a straight ahead Twitty fan, loved 'Only Make Believe' and 'Lonely Blue Boy' from his rock days and his later revealing Country songs like 'Lying Here Beside You (with Linda on my Mind)' or 'You've Never Been This Far Before'.

From the beginning I was riveted by his name and when I found that he was *not* born Conway but plain old Harold Jenkins my respect for the man doubled. Anyone who can *choose* to call himself Conway Twitty had got to be a man among men. On the road, as Harold, a pin was stuck into a map of their itinerary and like some hillbilly ouija board it said Conway, Arkansas and Twitty, Texas. Thus it was written and thus he was for ever named. No, sir, Conway doesn't hold back. There's a gaudy recklessness about him, about his haircuts, his leisure park Twitty City, his sincerity and, of course, his emotionally charged singing.

It was his singing that kept the letter page full. For a long time in the *LBBN* there was a highly specialized and bitter controversy. It seems the CTAS was split down the middle between those who loved Conway's *Croak* and those who were fans of his *Groan*. There was a lot of quite technical discussion about the difference between the two, how he made the different sounds and the meaning of each within the song. For the most part those who favoured the Groan couldn't stand his Croak ('Why, oh why does he have to Croak like that all the time? Oh, Conway, give us more groans, please, and leave all that horrrible croaking for the frogs.') and the other way round. I loved the fact that someone could be a big fan of Conway's *despite his constant croaking*. It's great to see such specific passion about such esoteric detail. They could have been lepidopterists talking about the Ulysses Blue.

☆ ★ ☆

Years later when I was pleased and proud to meet Conway on the front porch of his southern mansion-style home in the centre of Twitty City, his beautiful leisure park just outside of Nashville ('I made it for *you*, for my *fans*'). I was able to ask him about his Croak and his Groan. He didn't immediately understand what I was asking, so I tried to croak and groan for him but I was so choked up at being with the Master that it was all I could do to manage to push out a strangled wheeze.

I tried again and just about managed to groan.

'Oh,' he said, 'that's just a way I have of singing.'

Thanks, Conway. We'll try on more orthodox lines.

'Well, Conway, what's the greatest moment in your life?'

Very low, very sincere. The killer.

'I HOPE I HAVEN'T HAD IT YET.'

Green, Green
☆
Grass of Home

Hank's first appearance in Britain was at Bungay May Horse Fair barely two months after he arrived back in Wangford in 1976. Bungay had snoozed for hundreds of years by the dawdling waters of the River Waveney which ran along the Norfolk–Suffolk border. It was a dark and dotty little town and the whole area around had been unhinged for generations. It was this East Anglian lunacy which had attracted so many people to this part of the world in the first place. A Horse Fair sounded like just the right bit of madness to greet the lengthening days.

It had been a fine May day with a charge of spring fever in the air. One of those days when you just can't tell what's going to happen next. Something to do with the mixture of horses and dogs and people. The travellers, gypsies and didekei had come from all over East Anglia and some from even further afield. Now, in a moist, green field just outside the old town they all mingled with the local Hippies who had brought the Fair together.

By then the Sixties were only six years gone and the romantic and communal spirit was still alive in an extended community in that part of East Anglia centring on the Waveney. It was a mixture of local people who had been brought up in the area and middle-class towns-folk who had moved up there, hoping perhaps to plant some new roots in the countryside. Some still naïvely nurtured the alternative Sixties' ideals of side-stepping society. Being a bit of an old Hippie myself I had been drawn up there since 1974.

Now on a cool spring evening two years later I was standing in a dark, dank field waiting to see Hank do his stuff. Having met him only seven weeks before and been shaken by the bizarre correspondences of our lives and our dental profiles, I felt quite involved as I had suggested to him that he do his first gig at the Horse Fair, and had got him to meet my friends Andy and Sandra Bell. Andy was a gardener who drummed with various groups. He liked to look at the sky as regularly as possible. Luckily he had eyes that looked off in opposite directions so he could look at you and the sky at the same time. Sandra got excited about a Wangford gig at the Horse Fair and put it in the Waveney Clarion, the local alternative monthly magazine. And Andy said he'd be happy to play drums.

It was advertised for what it was, a homecoming gig for Hank who, although unknown then, was at least a local boy coming back after a long time in the States. He was going to do an evening show in the marquee after a whole programme of music from other bands. Out in the field there were several sideshows set among the wagons and carts, the traps and trailers. Lurchers, the travellers' hunting dogs, were everywhere, sniffing and snarling and shagging and racing rings round people's legs. Through the day, the normal business trading of a horse fair went on, horses and trailers inspected and admired, bought and sold. One cart, beautifully built and decorated by Keith Payne, was neither bought nor sold. Just stolen. The tension cranked up more and sparked every now and then as boys galloped breakneck through the people in the field. It was a heady day, with a hint of madness, lust and thieving simmering away below the surface. Just another spring day in East Anglia.

Many of the new community that had congregated in the area through the Seventies had some kind of connection with the travellers. The pull of the road was a strong one, and many had been restless for years before they came up to Suffolk. Some of the folks, like Keith, were involved in refurbishing wagons and carts, and there were a few showman's wagons parked outside several of the cottages and houses around. Many had horses without being part of a horsey set and most households had a lurcher or two.

The best of the sideshows set up by the born-again Country folk, the biggest pull of the afternoon by far, was the cancan. On a stage set out in the field half a dozen young maids and young mums danced, turned out impeccably in differently coloured satins and black trim, stockings and suspenders. Propriety was thrown bravely to the sharp east wind. Tantalizingly incongruous out in the open air, the girls shook their legs at the disbelieving travellers and gypsies. They did a raw and reckless cancan, whooping and shrieking as they lifted their skirts provocatively and flashed their frilly knickers or flew through the air and landed fearlessly in the splits on the rough wooden stage. They were – and there nearly was – a riot. Good ol' boys who had been stroking horses flanks and talking men's talk, surrounded by dogs shagging all day, could barely hold themselves back.

By the evening as we got closer to the gig, I was almost as nervous as Hank. Almost but not quite, for he was literally running round in circles. They were only circles of about a two-foot radius as he and most of the band were winding themselves up in a traveller's wagon out behind the marquee. I tried to calm them all down but it wouldn't work. Certainly Hank and Susie were both too nervous for that. Susie was the Big Mama of the cancan girls. She'd pushed them through it, drilled them and led them on. She was a brassy, sexy woman with big eyes and a big smile. One of those larger-than-life women, fiercely independent, who doesn't care what anybody thinks.

Susie came and joined for the night and brought Ginnie, one of her Girls and a singer with the Global Village Trucking Company, a commune-based group living in Church Farm, not far from that Bungay field. Susie and Ginnie looked stunning in their cancan gear and were the Jodrelles, the backing vocalists. We were surprised that Hank hadn't worried more, when the Colonel had suggested changing his name to Wangford, about the jerking off, the wanking, the masturbatory insinuations. *Resonances* we call them in the literary world. But he seemed unperturbed, shrugged his shoulders and said if that was the worst he had to deal with then where's the problem? So they were called the Jodrelles as confirmation. Rhyming slang, from the radio telescope at Jodrell Bank. Soon Susie became Susie Cruise and then later the Vera Lynn of the North Sea Oilfields. But for this initial gig she was, for the first time in your field tonight, simply a world-première Jodrelle.

Playing lead guitar and guiding the band musically was Mike Rogers, an old friend of mine from way before. Like me he had run to Suffolk as a refugee from an unhappy affair. Playing a sweet and seductive kind of rock, he was raised in folk and acoustic guitar picking. Playing Country music with Hank would be no problem. AB – Andy Bell – was on drums, clocking Hank and the roof of the marquee simultaneously and smiling transcendentally. Sitting behind his kit, he looked like a cross between Buddha and Chico Marx. A mate of his, Paul Fitzgerald, who had been playing bass in trios and bands in fairly horrible holiday camps and Country and Western clubs, turned up with his bass and amp in the back of his Morris van in case the fledgeling Wangfords wanted a bass player. They did, so he plugged in and got ready to busk.

All these people were onstage and waiting. The audience were waiting too and beginning to want to know why. Was this some kind of showbiz wind-up? In the middle of a field at a horse fair? Where was

Hank? The band were looking round a little anxiously and kept trying to smile hearteningly at the audience.

In fact Hank had lost his set list and I found him out in the back running round the field in a blind panic, scrabbling about in the dark. When I took him by the arm and guided him back to the wagon to calm him down we found the list sitting there where he'd left it on the side table. He grabbed it and ran.

He rushed on to the stage dramatically, waving his bit of paper with the set list like some kind of C & W Neville Chamberlain. He was wearing a very nasty silver-lurex cowboy shirt under my grey-striped dungarees with embroidered rose petals tumbling down one leg. Clashing hideously with the rustic romanticism of the dungarees and his battered old cowboy hat was a very nasty, shiny, gold-acetate windcheater with a fake rhinestone Golden Armadillo on the back. But the worst was yet to come, and half-way through the set he did a kind of Hillbilly strip, and tore off the gold windcheater and my dungarees to reveal an atrocious pair of what looked like loose-cut stainless-steel trousers. A symphony in silver. Pretty dumb, out in a muddy field, but Hank obviously thought it was great gear and pleased as punch said he'd got it all in a Black shop off Broadway in Nashville, perhaps the very one Elvis used to go to, as if that explained anything at all.

The gig was pretty *loose*, a bit of a busk from beginning to end, but surprisingly exciting and toe-tapping for all that. There was a lot of dancing, and one gypsy boy tore off his shirt and wailed away right in front of the stage for long enough to get the Jodrelles to notice his chest. The band was always on the edge, dangling over at times, but they never fell off somehow. They rocked out fiercely, and a lot of people grabbed each other and twirled around. Now and then Hank sang some good slow weepies, too, and there wasn't a dry eye in the tent. The Jodrelles sang so emotionally that everyone was cut to the heart. Here they were, these two cancan girls, and now they're singing Country music. There seemed to be some old songs and some originals, singer–songwriter style things like 'Jenny' or 'Hanging on to Columbia' and gut-wrenchers like 'Pain in My Wrist', a kind of Joe Tex Country-Soul number where the pain in Hank's wrist got so bad he broke down sobbing and collapsed. The Jodrelles picked him up in his time of need and brought him back to sing once again. It was very moving.

It was a good start.

After the gig, outside by the wagon, they talked about doing a few more gigs and seeing how it went. At least they'd try some rehearsals and get Paul worked in properly. And then they'd see. Susie had disappeared off with Dave the gypsy boy who had danced so manically in front of the band and didn't hear any of this until the next day.

Here's Dolly Parton and Steve Earle posing beside a wax model of Hank in a desperate attempt to be recognised.

It may be hard to believe, but Guy Mitchell, the last of the clean-cut pre rock 'n' rollers, was a big personal childhood hero of mine. In this picture I've smartened up specially to hide the ravages of the passing years to greet the great man.

"There are no strangers . . . . only friends we don't recognise." HW

Hank relaxes at a Rock 'N' Rodeo Nite

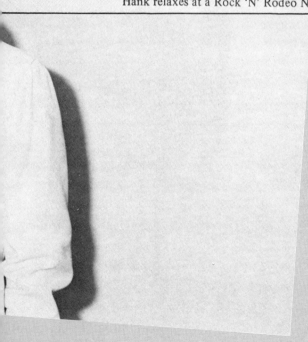

The first in our series of **THERE ARE NO STRANGERS** postcards which we sold on the **$incere Products** stall. You may be able to see the join, but Hank assures me that he was at Calgary.

The most successful of our THERE ARE NO STRANGERS series with me filling in for Hank, posing here in my pink suit with Ken Livingstone and Arthur Scargill, two of the finest Country singers in Britain today, as the unearthly glow round Arthur's serious Country & Western shows. We are at the GLC's Miners' Benefit Concert in 1984, just ten minutes before we encountered...

... the winner of the THERE ARE NO FRIENDS ONLY FASCISTS WE DON'T RECOGNISE competiti featuring the 'Skins against Honky-Tonk', an offshoot of the National Front. Who says music and politic don't mix?

Fastest Gun
☆
in the East

We rehearsed over at Hill Farm on the road to Beccles where both Andy and I were staying, so the drums were already set up there. Hank, Paul and Mike weren't far away. I could look after things, brew up for them while they rehearsed, which on sunny days was outside in the front garden. The first gig they did after Bungay was half a mile from Hill Farm, down Cucumber Lane on the vicarage lawn. It was the village fête and felt like an outdoor tea dance. The band were onlookers, set up on the side of the lawn. It was the second wildly incongruous gig out of two. Were the Wangfords already doomed to be permanently from another planet? Hard to tell. Like the first gig, it went well enough and so they looked for more. Paul had all the C & W connections and he checked some of them out. They eased their way into some little pubs, often set up in the corner by the dartboard. In not too long a time they were slipping into regular gigging. The Country and Western clubs started trickling in but as often as not went trickling out again. Right from the beginning the Wangs had problems convincing some of them that what they played *was* Country music.

The other band members were taken with Hank having changed his family name, Hardman, to a local village name, and decided they should all do likewise. Paul, who was born and bred in the area, became Roy Reydon. Andy, Andy Brampton. Mike became Norman after a blond-haired didekei who sang his heart out in a camp fireside musical

131

battle with the Romanies who had been step-dancing on a door set down on the ground. It was at one of the Barsham Faires in the late evening, and there was a feeling of a bit of aggro in the air. The Romanies were having a good night dancing on the door, clapping and cheering with the fire crackling away. Along came some travellers, the didicoys, to elbow their way in and break it up. Instead of bashing each other, the traveller boys pushed their Norman forward to sing. Like an angel, and with a heavenly little yodel in his voice, he soared out with one of the great country classics 'The Wild Side of Life':

'H-Aiyee didn't knoouuw God made Honky-tonk Angelllss . . .'

'Go, on, Norman!!! GOOoo on NORMAN!!!'

So Mike became Norman Uggleshall but it was a bit of a mouthful so he changed it to Weston which was much smarter.

☆ ★ ☆

Kessingland is a group of houses a couple of miles from Wangford, further up the A12 fish-finger run closer to Lowestoft. Hank bought his Gretsch Double Anniversary electric guitar in a junk shop there for sixty quid. Later he had his name inlaid up the fingerboard in mother-of-pearl. At heart, Hank is really a traditionalist.

The Wangfords also cut their eye teeth at Kessingland Working Men's Club where they would come on after the Bingo. They'd set up behind the curtain behind the Bingo caller. Then they'd pull the Bingo equipment aside, pull the curtains and there would be the Wangfords. BINGO! But they didn't seem to mind us too much and we did the gig several times. But the KWMC was the first time Hank dropped me in it.

Roy called me one day to say Hank had flipped out and had just slipped away. He'd mentioned something to somebody, but didn't directly tell the band he wasn't around. He said would I stand in for Hank. After all, I'd seen loads of gigs, been to rehearsals and could do a passable imitation so why not? We'd see if we could carry it off. I was game, and after all Kessingland wasn't too much of a risk so we thought we'd have a go.

It went fine and seemed to set an immediate precedent. Hank could be a moody and elusive bugger, like some kind of coypu disappearing off into the marshes. He said he didn't like playing Kessingland – 'It's a place for *buying* guitars, not *playing* them', so I got my understudy practices in after the Bingo.

Despite everything we started to get one or two semi-regular Country gigs. The most spectacular was the Bar H in the Hermanus holiday camp. The holiday camp itself was filled with small round toytown houses with conical roofs and looked like a reject set for 'The Prisoner'.

The Bar H was a weekly C & W and Cowboys and Indians meet.

The punters loved dressing Western and had all the gear. Some would be marshals, some deputies, some straight cowboys. Most were gun-slingers and used six guns which had been immobilized and couldn't fire live ammunition. Some of the girls were dressed as cowgirls, but nearly all of them were Indian maidens and wearing ersatz buckskins. There'd be lots of inter-racial fraternizing on the slow numbers, especially on 'He'll Have to Go', one of the great buckleshiners of all time. (The buckleshiner is the slow, close-held dance at the end of the evening when you sing along with the words of the song into your Indian squaw's ear, shining your Western-style belt buckle on her buckskins as you shuffle tight around the floor.)

The MC at the Bar H was Marshal Pete Wood, 'Fastest Gun in the East'. There had been shoot-outs, and Marshal Pete had cuttings of the newspaper stories to prove that no one was faster than he was this side of Newmarket. No, hold on, this side of *Cambridge*. He was good, the Marshal, and really got the punters going.

He had as bad an American accent as I did when I had to stand in for Hank, except his was more Suffolk. He had the six guns, the fine-tooled holsters tied round his thighs, the boots and an impressive stetson and fringed leather jacket. He looked great in front of the Wangfords doing one of his big request numbers, 'Ghost Riders in the Sky'. Hank was obviously pleased and proud to be backing Marshal Pete by the way he was shouting 'Yippee yi yay ... Har ... HAARRR!!' in the whip-cracking breaks at the end of the choruses.

In between the Wangfords' sets the fun really started. Some of the stuff was too arcane for any of us to watch. Hank crept up to the door and peeped in once, and they were lined up, the cowboys in a line opposite the Indian maidens and they all had their arms in the air. It had the mood of a masonic meeting and Hank knew that something very ancient was about to ritually unfold and felt it would be wrong for him to witness it. We may never know what happened.

Other times they had their shoot-outs, where they would have quick-draw competitions. They'd do the whole bit, staring each other down, legs apart, hands by their holsters. Then they'd draw and fire. We'd got used to the noise already because they liked to shoot off a few rounds in the style of the frisky young cowpokes just got into town *while we were playing*. This would happen on songs that they recognized or songs that mentioned cowboys. Marshal Pete would get drowned out by frenzied shooting and a lot of yahooing and yeehawing on Ghost Riders. It was at the Bar H that 'Cowboys Stay On Longer' really took off and after a couple of times they got right into it. We'd have a full gun battle on all the way through the chorus but especially on the hook line.

The third time we did it, the hook line Cowboys stay on Longer

133

sounded like the Alamo's last stand. I kept expecting John Wayne to come stumping in with his Davy Crockett hat.

The high spot of the evening was always the Killing of Ned Kelly where all the cowpokes lined up in a semi-circle and one of Marshal Pete's mates would come into the room dressed as the legendary Australian outlaw. He was wearing a dustbin and had a tin can on his head. He walked into the semi-circle, the cowpokes drew their guns, shot a lot of blanks at him and he fell down dead. Then they dragged him out of the room. Simple. That was it. Perfect.

Then the Wangs would come on for their third set. It was usually three fifty-minute sets with twenty-minute breaks at the C & W clubs. They would regularly run out of songs and have a lot of 'request' numbers in the third set. 'San Antone Rose', the classic from Bob Wills and his Texas Playboys, would always get a second airing.

'Thank you, thank you, thank you. Now here's a request for someone's favourite number that we did way back when we first started playing to you good people tonight, 'Dim Lights, thick Smoke and loud, loud Music'. All right, boys and girls, let's go!'

☆ ★ ☆

Even more surreal than the killing of Ned Kelly were the clubs that had harsh safety regulations about the firing of blanks. There is a small piece of wadding in blanks which can sometimes shoot out of the gun. Unlikely as most of the six guns they used in the clubs had barrels which were blocked. Nevertheless in these clubs the folks weren't allowed to point the guns at each other. Here's where we moved into another reality. In a shoot-out, two guys would stare each other down, walk slowly step by macho bow-legged step towards each other and stop ten yards apart. They'd keep on staring and scowling as the tension wound up. Eyeball to eyeball.

Then they'd draw. But because of the regulations, they couldn't actually *point* their guns at each other. So what did they do then? Simple – they drew their six-shooters from their holsters and with the barrel still pointing at the floor, *they would shoot the floor*. A bizarre sight, like castrated gladiators.

Luckily by the time Hank graduated, or degenerated, to the air bases the band knew far more songs. Luckily because there they wanted four sets. But the Wangs still didn't know all the *right* ones and they still had to do some 'requests' in the last set. As ever, they still did 'San Antone Rose' twice.

At one base they nearly got lynched. It might have been Bent waters or even Lakenheath, right by Wangford Fen, no relation, but it was certainly the Saturday night dance for the American Air Force Military Police. These guys were young, big, homesick and drunk. The all had early George Jones flat tops and mostly came from Tennessee. Hank knew he was in trouble even before the final request for 'Rocky Top'. It was bad enough the Wangs wouldn't do 'Orange Blossom Special', 'You Are My Sunshine' or even 'I Walk the Line' but no 'Rocky Top' was the real killer.

'You don't do "Rocky Top"?!' the six-foot-six seventeen-year-old, seventeen-stone sergeant from Tennessee asked incredulously. Luckily for us his legs buckled under him before he could manage any serious damage with his beer can. A couple of cans got thrown here and there but it was all a bit half-hearted. But the reverberations of not doing 'Rocky Top' were too strong and the air of menace grew. The Military Policemen weren't happy at all and it wasn't difficult to tell. When it came time to go, the boys suggested we leave as soon as possible.

'In fact, if you didn't have that young lady with y'all, why, y'all wouldn't be gittin' off of this base at aalll.'

On the Road Again

Long before the Wangs were being threatened at air bases they had to sort out their transport. A flotilla of Morris Minors was all very well but got less and less practical the further afield they went. Paul – Roy Reydon – had valuable contacts in the underbelly of the East Anglian motor trade and found an ex-GPO Ford Transit parcel van, the kind with the oversize body, up in Kirby Cane just the other side of the Waveney. It cost two hundred pounds, and when they realized the amount of money they were investing the band knew that they were getting serious.

The van became the Wangmobile, and soon there were plans to paint it. Hank was pushing for it to have huge, gaudy cowboys riding bucking broncos that flew across the sides of the van with flames blazing from their hooves. Paul advised against it and said it would make the Wangs sitting ducks for every jam sandwich – the white police cars with the red stripe along the side – out cruising the A12. He said that a psychedelic bronco buster on the Wangmobile wall would get them stopped six times a day.

So it was decided to keep it sober, and the van was painted black. They thought they'd call it the Wangford Bakery van. It could have a quote on it from Hank like 'All you need is Bread'. I was there when the band fantasized about all the details of what they could have on the Wangmobile. So was Tim Hunkin, a wonderful eccentric inventor, looking every inch the mad professor. Tim was not in the least mad, but was one of the few remaining specimens of a dying breed, the British Boffin. He had been doing the Rudiments of Wisdom, a quirky cartoon strip for kids in the *Observer* which told them how things worked. He listened quietly as everybody raved on and said nothing. The next morning when everybody got up we found Tim had painted on both sides in large square white letters:

WANGFORD BAKERIES

Underneath it on one side there was a caricature of Hank with:

Hank Sez : All You Need Is Bread

On the back doors he had fleshed out one of Hank's more obscure fantasies. There was a picture of an American-style white-sliced loaf, the kind with the real, soft, rubbery slices. Two of the slices were bending over, falling away from the loaf. Out of the slices and the loaf musical notes were pouring and floating up and away over the roof. Under this apparition was the legend:

The Only Genuine Country and Western Loaf

All the Wangs were surprised and delighted. The New Wang-mobile stood there, proud and shiny, a born-again bakery van. The cover was fantastic, and few guessed it was a band van. It was almost too good in the immediate vicinity and many times when they stopped to fill up the garage man would say:

'Wangford Bakeries? Have they started again? Why, I reckon last time I heard of them going was 1937. Have you got any hot and crusty in the back there?'

The band would have to explain that they were right out of hot and crusties but they'd bring some next time round. But the cover was impeccable as far as the old Bill was concerned. They only got stopped twice in nearly two years. Once was at about three in the morning, going down one of the Suffolk lanes coming back from a gig. Almost home, the Wangmobile was stopped by a solitary copper. He was friendly enough but kept sniffing the thick, heady air in the van as he asked them what they were doing, where they were going, oh! and they were *musicians*, were they, and where had the gig been? And all the time he asked his questions he was peering round, sniffing, sussing, wondering.

'So what kind of music do you lads play,' he opined, 'Rock 'n' Roll?'

'Oh, no, officer, Country and Western.'

In the twinkling of a twinkling eye he turned back into the per-sonification of a lovable British bobby, drew back, took his foot out of the van, waved them on cheerily and said

'Oh, that's all right then, lads. Well, you'd better be getting home, now. Mind how you go.'

You see. With its roots in mums' and dads' bargain bins in the record shops, C & W has got to be eminently safe and acceptable.

Sometimes that's a blessing in disguise, and the lesson to be learned here for would-be musicians is to always say Country and Western in any dealings with the law, customs or immigration. Better safe than sorry. After all, the worst that can happen is you'll get sneered at, and if you can't cope with that you shouldn't be a muso.

Many of the musos on the Country and Western circuit did some sneering of their own, obviously despising the audience they were playing to. Sometimes Hank got very depressed by their contempt for the C & W fans. Later, I tried to reason with him and said that if the option otherwise was to work in a pea-freezing plant or a fish-finger factory then maybe it was fair enough. But he rightly pointed out to me that that was no excuse for that kind of attitude towards the punters, that however dumb they might be, they're never as dumb as you think. No one deserves to be despised like that. And, just as important, no one can play real music with that much contempt in their heart. That's what bothered Hank about the Country scene. He saw it as music with no life and with no love, played by dead people to people who wanted nothing more than to hear all their old favourites. A song sung without love can never be more than a cardboard cut-out. That way it would stay forever dead and never move on. All of that is no reason to avoid playing new stuff. There will always be someone out there who can move on beyond Charley Pride.

Ten years on, more and more rock fans are listening to Country, seeing it as another roots music, and are probably Keeping It Country more than many of the diehard British C & W fans who in that time have inherited Boxcar Willie and, God help them, Barbara Mandrell.

As the Dalai Lama Jnr, Nepal's finest ever C & W stylist, says:

'It's karma, man, that's what it is. And it always catches up with you. KARMA.'

☆ ★ ☆

There are a few contenders for the worst Wangford gigs of this period. There were three C & W clubs that they managed to empty. Neither Hank nor I can remember their names or where they were. Selective memory. But at all of them the punters, deciding the Wangfords weren't going to play their favourites, started to get up and leave. Slowly at first, but soon the trickle became a flood. Hank had disappeared for three days before one of them and I had to stand in for him. The moment you realize in the middle of a number that you're playing to no one, that everyone's gone home, is one of those times again when time stands still and you ask yourself Universal Questions. A moment to come to terms with yourself. You begin to understand the pain, what it's all about, and the suffering of Country and Western really comes home.

The Casbah in Lowestoft, one of the earliest gigs, was a little coffee bar in the most easterly point of the British Isles. For all its eastern and moorish arches, though, it was still more Lowestoft than Tangier, more fish fingers than couscous. It was no less depressing than the rest of Lowestoft, and the Wangs played cowering in a corner until they were allowed to go home.

In Norwich was a typical East Anglian ballroom, originally tatty but now faded, that had a heart-stopping slogan.

The Gala Rooms were, it announced:

A Nice Place to take The Wife

They played an anonymous pub, probably called the Red Bull, a lot of them are, right on a roundabout in the middle of a council estate off the M4, half-way to Bristol. It hardly paid anything, but Hank thought it would be 'Good on-the-road experience'. The rest of the Wangs tended not to agree, especially Susie Cruise who always did the last, late-night leg of the drive back home. The boys would all be crashed out in the back. Hank had it all worked out and would do the first leg before he disappeared in a cloud of smoke. Roy would start to nod over the steering wheel and Susie would push him aside and take over. She was too nervous to let any of the rest do it.

And down in the M4 council-estate pub, no one, road experience or no road experience, really enjoyed playing to a bunch of grannies with their sherries, or the yobbos playing pool down at the end of the room. The Wangs found it pretty surreal as the wall at the opposite end of the room – the wall they were playing to – was glass and looked directly out on to the roundabout. It wasn't until the third set that they could cope with singing to the cars as they went round the roundabout and whizzed past the pub. It took that long to accept traffic as Part of Life.

But the Wangs came back all the same and justified it next time by turning it into a mini-tour and doing the next night down at a glass-works social club on Basingstoke industrial estate. There was a lovely unexpected buzz at the glass works when a couple of paraplegics came out on to the dancefloor in their wheelchairs and jived with a standing partner. They swung round in their chairs, side to side and going under their partner's arm by practiced jive control of their wheels. One even did wheelies.

It was the glamour of life on the road that drove the Wangfords on.

Whisky on my Guitar

Hank loves singing though he has always been acutely aware of his limitations. The Colonel and I both tell him he's too self-deprecating and has a nice voice but he won't listen. Either way, he doesn't stop singing whatever anyone says and agrees with Van Holyoak, an old cowboy singer who said:

> *Everybody ought to sing all the time. If the Good Lord gave*
> *you a good voice, it's the best way there is to say thanks. If*
> *he never, it's a damned good way to get even.*

Then anytime Hank wanted to stop singing for a while, he'd simply disappear. He was staying at his mother's in Wangford quite a lot when he wasn't being a dirty stop-out, but when he went under cover he was untraceable for days or even weeks. I tracked him down once after ten days when he had retired in the middle of winter to be at one with the sea.

Southwold is a sleepy, neatly trimmed little coastal town where people retire to listen to the sea. Time has been recycled here for the past hundred years and more. Its streets have the special smell of beer brewing by the seaside, the sharp tang of brine mixed with the blowsiness of hops from Adnams' brewery. The town is built along a long stretch of desolate pebbly beach, a wintry no-man's-land between the whistling emptiness of Suffolk and the wind-whipped swells of the grey-brown North Sea. On a clear day the dismal concrete slab that is Sizewell nuclear power station looms southerly a few bare, blank miles down that beach, its grey modernity blending in horribly well with the ineluctable loneliness of the East Anglian coastline.

140

Built along the beach in front of the town is a line of well-kept and sought-after beach huts, living relics from a bygone age. Used for changing by those foolhardy enough to want to plunge into the murky brown of the sea, they are more commonly for sitting in, brewing up and looking out with a nice cup of tea in the hand at the icy waves battering the bleak coastline. Down the beach towards the sorry remains of Southwold pier is another group of huts, much shabbier in 1977 and not as salubrious a neighbourhood as the pristine beach palaces revelling in names like Ocean Waves, Sea View or Try Again. This little group had a western theme with names like Laramie, Klondyke or Abilene. They looked fittingly more like prospectors' shacks than beach huts. They were pretty run down and one was even leaning over at a dangerous-looking angle.

It was in Klondyke, next door to the lean-to, that I found Hank after he'd gone to ground for ten days. I was walking down the beach with my face stung by the maddening east wind. This wind doesn't stop at the beach but slices across East Anglia and the Fens, and comes from beyond the Baltic, beyond the heart of the Russian steppes or even the northern tundra of Siberia. It probably comes direct from the Russian satellites out in space. It certainly feels like it.

Over the wailing of the wind I thought I could hear something like a guitar as I passed the western stretch. I went over to Klondyke and heard what sounded more like a campside ukulele. When I pressed my ear to the wall I could hear it was Hank. He was singing 'Bury me not on the Lone Prairie' and changing the words around to 'Bury me not in the Deep, Deep Sea'. I knocked on the door and the playing stopped. After a while of knocking and shouting through the door that it was me, Hank opened the door, shot anxious glances each way, grabbed me by the arm and yanked me in quickly.

'Watch out, they'll see you,' he hissed.

'Oy, watch it. Hold on there, Hank. What do you mean they'll see me? Who'll see me. What's the problem?'

'No problem, no problem at all, it's just anyone might see you. And then they'll figure out that I'm here and I just don't want anybody to know I come here. I know you know, but you don't need to tell anybody.'

'But why must it be such a big secret?'

'Look, don't you understand? It's my bolt hole, I've got to have a bolt hole. I need my privacy for Chrissakes. I have to be alone sometimes and if I've gotta squat on the beach to do it, that's the way it is.'

I looked around as my eyes got accustomed to the dark. It looked pretty rough in there, but at least Hank had a mattress, bedclothes, a table and chair and a little camping stove. Not much floor space left. I crouched on to the chair.

'Yeah, yeah, I know it's tight, but I'm real comfortable here. I keep quiet at nights 'cos I know I'm not supposed to stay here overnight. I've just needed to think about things. And write some songs. Have the gigs been OK? You're handling them all right?'

All right?! What does he mean 'all right'? I felt like screaming at him after he just walked out and expected us all to just get on with it. But I could see that the man was having a hard time with himself. I saw a couple of empty whisky bottles and decided to leave him be.

'Yes, we're OK I suppose. Missing you, though, but you know that, you bastard. I'm trying but I can only do so well. I still haven't got it covered like you have.'

'That's because you haven't had the experience, but all this will be good for you, tighten you up.'

'Oh, yeah? Tighten us up? Ha, I tell you, I don't know what good some of the gigs would do anybody. I mean, going nearly two hundred miles to play to a bunch of grannies on a council estate, that's one *you* didn't fancy much . . .'

'Yeah, OK, I'm sorry about that one, but they're all experience of one kind or another. And I'll be back in a coupla days, ready for the gig on Friday. Where is it?'

'In Norwich. The Jacquard.'

'Listen, if we've got time, maybe we can rehearse. I've got a new song. Listen. Sorry it's just the uke, but I haven't got the guitar 'cos there's no point, you can't really swing it around here in Klondyke like you can the uke. Anyway, you can still hear the song.'

And he sang me 'Whisky On My Guitar' for the first time.

> *Whisky on my guitar and an aching in my head,*
> *I spilt my soul, I lost control,*
> *At the words I heard you said.*
> *Whisky on my guitar and the Devil in my heart*
> *Oh, Lord, You'd better rescue me*
> *Before I fall apart.*
>
> © Chappell Music and $incere $ongs

And we did get the new song rehearsed in time for Norwich. And it sounded good. I didn't tell anyone else where he had disappeared to but I kept my eye on him. The empty bottles had worried me and for a man who professed to prefer the weed to the booze it certainly looked like he could be slipping into a not-too-secret drinking problem.

It got worse, not better. His later battles with the bottle got more and more heroic. After the strange chaos of Easter '78, lurching from hard-rock heaven to hillbilly hell, we found him going off on increasingly long binges. His disappearing at the drop of a hat and leaving me to stand in for him at no notice just got all the Wangfords disillusioned. Without him the heart had gone out of it. Even the lure of taking Country music to the Punks and Rock 'n' Rollers didn't get us going. Hank was always more of a crusader than I was.

However I might have tried to cover for Hank at the gigs, we all began to feel we were treading water and stagnant water at that.

I've seen selective deafness in action at Wangford gigs. Susie sang a song of Hank's called 'A Hard Man is Good to Find', a play on Hank's old name and an old Mae West line turned into a Percy Sledge style of song. Ms Cruise, dressed like a bar-room whore, would give it a lot of stick and be very indelicate. The song was a slow and dramatic 6/8, which is like 3/4, a waltz. And while Susie sang her lungs out, the mums and dads, the Crimplene Cowboys, would waltz incongruously around and not hear a damn thing.

'You Never Can Tell' is an old Chuck Berry tune that has become part of the Country Rock repertoire. Emmylou Harris did a great version of it early on. The hook-line in the chorus goes:

> *C'est la vie, say the old folks,*
> *It goes to show you never can tell.*

Imagine our surprise when one night in the Queen's Head, Sax-mundham, a regular gig for the Wangfords, we saw a band, I think they were 'Barry and the Night Riders', singing what they thought the chorus was saying:

> *Tel Aviv, say the old folks,*
> *It goes to show . . .*

Kinky Friedman, the Jewish Texan Country star, writer of classics like 'Ride 'Em Jewboy' and 'Asshole from El Paso', would have been pleased and proud. He might even have *schlepped nachis.*

The Fool
☆
on the Marshes

Bulcamp House sits on a spit of land which pushes out into the tidal marshes between Southwold and Blythburgh. It is an astonishing open and beautiful position. Twice every day it was in the middle of mud marshes and twice a day it was surrounded by sea. It changed every time you looked at it, it came and went so fast. It was always different and always the same and always surrounded by a great deal of space.

For a year I lived in the house itself along with ten other people in a kind of community. My son Mathew came to live with me near the end of that year while his mum went to America to put down new roots. He stayed over a year and went to the little local village school in Wenhaston where he was the forty-ninth pupil. I was going to London every week for two days to do six clinics at the Clinic which earned me enough to live. I could see Mat into bed on the Tuesday night and be back on Thursday to see him before he went to sleep. It couldn't have been done without help from the others. Many souls passed through Bulcamp House. It was like a rest home, a recovery centre. It was, to many of us, our Alma Mater.

It was fairly egalitarian and communal. There were usually a couple of lurchers at Bulcamp, so we hunted and had a regular supply of hare and rabbit. Everybody took a turn at cooking, doing the lot for one night, buying all the food and cooking and serving it. I was pretty terrible and mostly stuck with spaghetti and soup. Paul Fitz got inspired by curries. Simon Loftus, who owned the main body of the house, usually cooked on Sundays and always did us proud. An ascetic *bon vivant*, Loftus would treat us all to sturdy country *haute cuisine* with fine wines. A delight. Sandra Bell was the poorest of us all, so as well as an occasional rabbit or hare, which would always be tasty, she'd do comfrey fritters, which were not. Comfrey is also called symphytum or boneset and the leaves are traditionally used in poultices and infusions to help broken bones knit together. Sandra would deep-fry the leaves, found by paths and roads, in batter. Full of iron, we were told, but that didn't make them taste any better. Even deep fried in batter, they'd probably be better as poultices.

☆ ★ ☆

In the second year Mat moved into the east end of Bulcamp, Tim Hunkin's part. I moved out into a showman's wagon sitting outside the house in the meadow on the marshes, open to the full force of the elements. I bathed and ate and cooked in the house itself, but slept, wrote, worked, played and drank tea out in the wagon. If Hank came down from his mother's in Wangford we'd drink more than tea. I may have been in the wagon but I certainly wasn't *on* it. It had been parked there by Peter Biziou. Being a fine cameraman and much in demand, whizzing about the world doing commercials and feature films from New Mexico to New Zealand, he was rarely there and was happy for me to look after it and keep it warm.

A showman's wagon is a long trailer that the travelling people – fairground operators and circus folk – live and move around in. These days they are glittering giants, great chrome palaces on wheels, but Biziou's came from the Thirties when they were made of wood or metal and painted dark colours, often greens, burgundies or browns. They looked more like small train carriages than caravans, without the bow tops or the gaudy bravura of gypsy decorations. Inside, this one was panelled in wood with unfussily etched windows. It was modest and comfortable. It had a door that came in through the kitchen at one end, a central living-room with a coal- and wood-burning stove, and a bedroom at the other end. Evenings were spent by candlelight and paraffin lamps. I slept by a window and each morning by raising my head a tad, without even getting out of bed, I could look out and stare God straight in the eye through either a summer morning's Elysian serenity or the Siberian hell of a howling wilderness.

The meadow was exposed on three sides to the marshes. It was the first on the spit to get the arctic blast of the north-east winds smack in the face. It did get very cold. But even when it was way below zero outside, when the ground was frozen and crunchy underfoot, when icicles hung over the windows and angry squalls whipped and tore like shrieking banshees at the wagon, inside by a roaring fire it was the cosiest place in the world. Only on a winter morning, after looking out of the window with the blankets up to my chin and urging the Supreme Being to Have a Nice Day, was it a bit spartan hopping across the icebox of the living-room to put the kettle on and rekindle the cold, charred remnants of last night's fire.

Three miles across the bare marshes, Southwold shone brave and white. To the right the sweep of the Walberswick woods. There was a big dead tree near the banked up edge of the meadow, the sea wall. And a crazy horse called Dobbin. There were three or four wagons and caravans at different times out on the meadow. As soon as Dobbin saw anyone coming out of the wagon or into the field, he would gallop full tilt at them, dodging at the very last moment, lurching ludicrously close to them, staring with his wild eyes to see if he'd got through, if they were looking scared. He scored with Hank who regularly looked scared.

The Blythburgh marshes were the stopping-over point for millions of migrating birds. Some nights, when the marches were packed wing-to-wing, beak by jowl, the noise out there in the dark space of the flat Suffolk countryside was deafening. Ten million birds chirruping, twittering, squawking and cackling, fighting, warbling and shrieking, churring and whirring, eating, chewing, cooing and cawing, clucking and hooting, piping and crowing and screeching. It went on all night with no respite. When it's rush hour like that out on the marshes they call it the Parliament of Birds. And that's just what it was, noisier than Question Time in the Commons after some governmental scandal has broken. Order! . . . ORDER!! . . . *ORDER!!!*

It was a crossroads for flocks of birds, some flying north, some south, all converging on these coastal marshes. The cacophony would echo off the woods on the other side of the marshes by Walberswick. Sitting in the wagon I wondered what the birds were saying. Travellers' tales? Air traffic down the long corridors south? England's chances in the next European Cup? They certainly sounded like gelded football hooligans at times, and often made as much noise as the Canaries' fans up in Norwich's friendly little ground at Carrow Road.

Like Saskatchewan and Skye, these Suffolk marshes were the land of the imagination. More like the watery vastness of Norfolk than the cosier parts of Suffolk, the marshes had an emptiness that the mind could drift off into. Skye has very few trees, just its peat bogs and moorlands, and the intimidating lunar contortions of the Black Cuillin. Suffolk is flat like Saskatchewan and has something like the big sky of the Prairies. Not quite as expansive perhaps, but empty enough to let the mind wander. And wander it does; there is a tradition, probably as much to do with the infuriating winds as the endless sky, of poetic lunacy out on the flats of East Anglia. Through the years it has had its fair share of deranged philosophers and visionary poets as well as conventional psychotics. Certainly I became a little unhinged in my year out in the wagon, but it's perfectly normal to be a crackpot round these parts.

Some say it's the sky or the light that loosens people's screws. There's certainly a lot of it about. It even gets into the Suffolk churches which are famous for their light, glorifying the noumenal luminance of the East Anglian skies. A lot of them have extra clerestory windows high up above the nave which light up the ceiling. Blythburgh Church, the Cathedral of the Marshes, is a wonderful example of this, with a ceiling so airy and light it looks like it is flying away on the slender wings of its wooden angels. The nearest thing to being open to the sky you can get with a roof on.

Which is what living in a wag does for you. Closer to the sky. You know why the Indians loved their tepees, the Mongolians their gers or yerts. You see why gypsies and travellers, tinkers and sailors are so loopy. It's the skies. Skies all the time. And it's the winds, and the noise of the winds. The winds that come out of the skies.

It was during this second year, from '77 into '78, that my relationship with Hank turned right round. When we first met in that pub in Wangford over a year before, he was a rock. He carried me through some difficult times. I looked on him as a father and he filled the role well. He'd seen it all before. He'd seen the inside of the divorce courts more times than I'd had Sara Lee Cheesecake with blueberry topping and he'd survived, hadn't he? Best of all, he had the ability to laugh at himself when everything was looking black. So I trusted him with my fears and he respected my trust.

But during my year on the marshes I got stronger as Hank wore down. He began to fall apart in the way parents do when they became senile. I don't know why, whether it was lost love or lost dreams, but he started to become a child and our roles, as so often happens with fathers and sons, were reversed. He fell apart bit by bit and became more fractious, more insecure, more selfish, more *babyish*. He regressed right back and started demanding instant gratification. It was as if this late in life he was being wrenched from the tit, and was having difficulty adjusting. If there wasn't a breast available, then the bottle would have to do . . . So he started going off on binges, disappearing for days on end and missing gigs. But it didn't work. It never does.

Tonight the Bottle let me down . . .

I became *his* rock and had to patch him together more than a few times. Many times through the winter he would stay over in the wag, dossing down like a sack of rags in a sleeping-bag on the floor in front of the fire. He would bring some whisky, teach me some old Country songs and maybe a new one of his. Occasionally we wrote some together. Then he'd drink himself to sleep. There was always a stack of empty bottles in front of the cold, silent burnt out stove any time Hank had been over.

☆ ★ ☆

Bulcamp House is an old rambling farmhouse with two storeys, two wings, two kitchens, a cottage attached out back and a maze of delightful old rooms with wonky floors. It is long and low and it has a great and benevolent character. Outside, round the yard, were barns, workshops, toolsheds and stables. When Bulcamp was really going full tilt there would be things happening everywhere with somebody tapping, cutting or sloshing away in every barn or workshop, behind every door.

Several people, like Keith, Sue, Stevie or Andy, were in the barns, refurbishing and decorating traps and trailers, caravans and pony carts. Susie was in her workshop doing her sculpting – a large many-headed horse for George Harrison's Dark Horse records, and some gnomes for his garden. Paul would be in a barn under a Morris Minor. Hunkin was in his own workshop making little machines, exotic little inventions straight from Professor Branestawm. His little wooden people did ingenious things with pennies like sideshows in an Edwardian penny arcade. They were sculptures of his Rudiments of Wisdom cartoon people, caricature ectomorphs like naïve Modiglianis.

For a long while, Hunkin worked with Wilf Scott as a pyrotechnician. Barsham Faires, the great community celebrations we held every August, like Christmas in mid-summer, were graced through the years with some ecstatically wacky firework displays from Phlegethon Fireworks. In 1975, at the top of Barsham Field, set out on a great frame, we had a huge, blazing Sun with a grinning mouth that opened up. The climax was when a Great Fiery Dragon, spitting lightning and belching fire, flew out of the sky on a Kamikaze dive towards the Sun. The Dragon hung on cables that ran from a high pine tree across the Barsham field to the face of the grinning Sun. A good number of us pulled on ropes to drag the Fearsome Beast on its last flight to the Centre of the Sun. It was an awesome Dragon and its jaws yanked open and closed as it roared and spluttered its way across the night sky. Rockets shot out of it, flares vomited from its waggling mouth but it managed to hold together all the way to its fateful collision . . . it picked up speed on its last stretch, diving headlong out of the night and then *Whoooff!!!* It all went up in a huge fireball as the Dragon burst into the Sun.

It may have been cosmic, the two forces of nature coalescing in a final flameout and all that, but to me it was just like a gigantic incendiary head butt.

There were times everyone worked together if a huge commission came in. Wilf and Tim had to make floating polythene sheep and pigs for the Pink Floyd. That meant a lot of work round Bulcamp for a lot of hands. Hundreds of mortars were packed with inflatable sheep and pigs. Each had to be folded and packed in exactly the right sequence so that they would fill up with air after they had been shot high out of the mortar at its zenith and billow out to float down peacefully to the ground.

Which is exactly what they did when we tried them out over the marshes by the wagon behind the barns. They burst out of the mortars above our heads, rippled open and hung knowingly in the sky, hovering for a while. As they floated down, rocking gently in the breeze, they seemed to be gazing contentedly across the marshes to the sea, looking as if they didn't have a care in the world.

At the end of the stables, by the path that ran from the East End to the meadow, was the Tack room. It was a small wood-lined room that was away from the main house but could be warmed fairly easily. It became the Wangfords' rehearsal room and storage space. It held the heart of the band. And for quite a while the band was based at Bulcamp. Rehearsals in the Tack room were the easiest I have known. It was a cosy little room and the wood walls gave the sound a warm feel. It was grand to be in the country, too, and be able to take a whiff of sea air between numbers.

As Hank was increasingly taking a back seat and I was getting more involved with the band, I was grateful for the time available to rehearse and feel out numbers and ideas. It was country time not city time which meant . . . more time. That can be good or bad. It usually means things take longer. Sometimes they don't even happen. But at best it gives things a chance to develop naturally, and even if it sounds like Hippieshit, to grow *organically*. So the band had the time in the Tack room to explore Country music and our feelings about it as Hank slipped away. Even without him around we all knew we liked it and wanted to play it but had to find out how we would play it. We were strongly influenced by Commander Cody and Conway Twitty from Hank and Gram Parsons and George Jones from me. They were honkytonkers, right from the beginning, those Wangfords.

But then it was *only semi-pro*. It had grown out of a bizarre horse fair in a field with the budding cancan girls. And rehearsals ever since, with either of the two main manifestations of the Wangfords, have always been hell. I only have myself to blame. Since I have taken over from Hank more and more I've allowed myself to be browbeaten by musicians. Although I've known for years that in medicine *experts* often put up smokescreens to hide the fact that they are bluffing, I've always had a musical inferiority complex and deferred to the *real* musos. It's as if I've still not learned punk music's iconoclastic lesson in 1976. Still, it all takes time.

Listen, Doc, all this Hippieshit and Social Realism is getting totally out of hand.

But that's what biography is all about.

I've told you before, Doc, I'm paying for this book so don't tell *me* what it's all about.

Colonel, I— . . .

Where are all HANK's great successes? What about his meetings with all the Country greats? His times with Willie, Tammy, Waylon, Buck or Dwight? We've gotta have something to hold on to, there's just too much *failure* around this bit. Lighten up.

But, Colonel, you can't *rewrite* the past.

Are you crazy? It happens all the time. So give us some action and a bit more Hank. You sound like you're trying to get rid of him . . .

Colonel, would *I* do that?

I'm warning you, Doc, I'm watching you.

Keep it Country!

Easter '78 was a turning point. Or at least the Wangfords finally found out, if they hadn't realized before, exactly who their audience was. They had played to all sorts before, from pub rock gigs to heartland C & W, from air-force bases to horse fairs and always preferred the rockier or hippier gigs. But Easter that year really spelled it out.

The year before they had played one of the most committed C & W clubs in East Anglia. It was beside the bridge at Potter Heigham right on the Norfolk Broads, in the wild and watery east, and was run by a Mrs Wigley who was so strict that no one even knew her first name. She was just Mrs Wigley. Maybe the thought of her was too much for Hank and he just went and disappeared again. So I stood in for him and the gig turned out to be an unhinging nightmare.

The club was a great cavernous barn of a place, a tall concrete structure which could hold at least five hundred Country fans, stetsons and all. It had a Western theme throughout, fairly half-heartedly done, with tatty cowboy motifs like wagon wheels on the walls and a long Western-style bar right down one side of the hall. There were tables and chairs spread through the hall with a clear dancing area in front of a high stage. It was like a cross between a Western saloon and a working men's club. Everyone serving at the bar had red-and-white-check shirts, and bandannas tied Gene Autry-style at the side of the neck.

We had barely arrived when a very small woman came scurrying nervously up to us in the corridor.

'Are you the band?' she asked in an unexpectedly Yorkshire accent and, not waiting for an answer, 'You *do* play Country and Western, don't you? That's what we have here at the club, you know. Only

Country and Western. You do know it's a Country and Western club, don't you?' Her words came tumbling out on top of each other, smothering themselves. She seemed to be teetering on the edge of panic. She was clocking the scruffiness and the jeans and saw we didn't have the green mohair suits . . .

I remember seeing an ad for a Country band on the C & W circuit featuring their greatest assets; it said they were

Professional
Smart
Punctual

and there was the picture of them in the suits to prove it.

'Nice group, aren't they? Very smart.'

'Yes, it's lovely to see the youngsters polishing their shoes just like we used to. And that beautiful crease in the trousers . . . coo, it takes you back all right.'

'I know. And I thought they started at a very nice time too.'

'They did, didn't they? Nice to see a group starting sharp at seven-thirty. None of that hanging around.'

'That's exactly what I say. And I loved the way they finished their first bit eight-fifteen right on the dot.'

'Yes, a good sense of timing, that's what's missing in a lot of music nowadays. I think we should have them back . . .'

Meanwhile, back at the Ranch, Mrs Wigley's eyes narrowed and she stared up at me suspiciously. She looked like she had big worries on her mind and would obviously need careful handling and a lot of reassurance. I could feel the Doctor welling up in me. She was the Monday-morning valium addict who had run out on Friday and I was the locum GP from another planet.

'You don't play Rock 'n' Roll do you? We can't have that. We won't like that. Only Country here. Country and Western.' She would have poked her head right up my nose if only she could have reached.

'M'am, you don't know how good that makes us feel to hear you say that,' I bullshitted in my best fake American Hank voice, 'Country and Western is what we like to play, and that's what we'll give you. No, m'am, no Rock 'n' Roll, don't you worry about a thing. But do you know there are some clubs on the so-called Country circuit,' I grasped her by the elbow in a semi-Wangford* and bent down towards her ear, 'some clubs where *they* ask *us* to play Rock 'n' Roll, where they want to hear Route 66 and Memphis Tennessee and suchlike. And we have to play them that stuff or they get real difficult . . . Call themselves Country? Hah! Shoot ma dog! We don't need all those Rock 'n' Roll requests. Let

*See p.156

them have a Rock 'n' Roll band if that's what they want. We wanna play Country and have a hard enough time finding places where we can do it without goddam – oh, 'scuse me m'am – without Country folks asking for Rock 'n' Roll. We wanna *Keep It Country*! We wanna see people doing the cotton-eyed Joe, not the boogaloo or jiving or whatever. I tell you m'am, it makes us so happy to hear you say those things, we're going to give you one hundred and fifty per cent Country and Western tonight.'

I stopped myself in my tracks, wondering if I had gone a little bit over the top. Mrs Wigley seemed only barely reassured but went off all the same, clucking and muttering to herself. We got on with setting up our gear and sound checking and didn't hear from her again until the actual gig. In spite of the impressive bravura of my sincerity, I had the feeling that she had me sussed. Still, it was going to be interesting if nothing else.

We started our first set as normal with '(Empty Bottle, Broken Heart and) You're Still On My Mind', remembering the first time Gram Parsons had shown me Country's fierce soul. It was the ritual opener. We liked to put our honkytonk cards on the table. Then we played a real Country loser's song 'She Thinks I still Care'. Recorded by lots of people including Elvis, it was a big hit for George Jones. I felt confident that we'd get through to them with this one, but no one got up to dance yet. The third was 'Whisky on My Guitar' a Wangford Hall of Pain standard that is not dissimilar to Harlan Howard's country classic 'Heartaches by the Number'. Roy Reydon on bass was singing lead and as I lurched into the harmonies on the first chorus I felt a tugging at my leg. I looked down.

The stage at Potter Heigham was higher than most, about five feet off the ground. Peering over the edge of it was Mrs Wigley's face contorted like the terrified Japanese peasant in Seven Samurai when he is told to go and kill the bandits with his home-made bamboo spear. Her left arm was tugging furiously at my jeans as she waved violently with the other. She was moving dangerously into adrenalin overload. Her eyes were staring and beginning to bulge out of her head. I could see from six foot away her pupils were dilated and she was mouthing something to me that I couldn't hear over the music.

If fish could drown, I thought, *this is what they'd look like.*

As soon as we came to the solo and I stopped singing, I bent over to hear what she was trying to say. I stuck my ear right by her mouth.

'NO, NO, NO,' she was croaking, 'COUNTRY AND WESTERN, WE MUST HAVE COUNTRY AND WESTERN.'

I was stunned.

I freaked. The blood drained into my cowboy boots.

I could feel myself going wobbly at the knees. As my legs started to buckle under me, there was a moment when I didn't know who I was, where I was or what the hell I was doing wherever it was I was doing it. If you know what I mean.

What is going on? What the hell is she talking about? Are we playing Country music or what? Can we never get it right? What more can we do – this is our third Country song out of three, what do they want for God's sake?

I was poleaxed but as our set and the evening wore on I began to get a glimmering of what was happening. In desperation Mrs Wigley had brought her son Michael onstage in the breaks between our sets. Michael Wigley sang and played guitar even worse than I did, but at least he sang all the songs that we'd missed out. He'd wanted to get up and do a number or two with us, one of the conditions of doing the gig, we had heard, but his mum wouldn't let him do it after hearing our first set. I could see quite clearly that what they meant by Country and Western was all the good old songs they knew and could sing along with, like 'He'll Have to Go', 'Rocky Top' or 'El Paso'. All great songs, but I didn't want to play dead copies. 'El Paso' was a bit long for Michael and he stuck with 'You Are My Sunshine'. In a Yorkshire accent.

Doc, I've gotta warn you – you musn't put down Promoters like you do. Not sensible.
Why not, if they deserve it?
Yeah, but they are our bread and butter. They are my personal *friends* and *colleagues*. Just take care not to butter the hand that feeds you or it might bite back . . .

All right, I should have realized, too, that it was pretty obvious we were far too loud for them, and our rhythm section too prominent for the ricky-tick kind of Country they liked. It may well have been Country we were playing, but it just had too much *bollocks*.

As for originals, well, ask any Country band. As deep in the heartland as we were that night you can risk one or two originals per set at the most. Anything by Charley Pride will usually get you out of the shit and Crystal Chandeliers will stop them in their tracks even if they're coming at you with pickaxes or real ammo in their six guns.

I'd sort of known all this and shouldn't really have been surprised. Hank himself had always been more conciliatory about it, saying that you had to take these folks by the hand and guide them ever so gently into any new areas, but I just didn't have the patience. There was nothing inherently wrong in them finding comfort in the familiar. I didn't feel patronizing towards them, I just didn't want to be the man to give them the safe, secure stuff they expected. Everyday music for everyday folks. Nor did I want to go on a self-conscious crusade to widen their outlooks or to show them that Country was much richer and more varied than they might have thought. It would be a crusade doomed to failure and they'd probably say that it wasn't Country and Western anyway.

☆ ★ ☆

If Colonel Frank doesn't object, I'll jump a decade for a taste of Volume IV here. Ten years after Mrs Wigley, when Hank's A to Z of C & W came out on television introducing some of the best and warning against some of the worst in Country, the reactions could have been predicted from that night in Potter Heigham. The C & W audience was split into for and vituperatively against Hank. While Wangford tried to show his favourite music to be made of many regional styles, with a heartfelt plea to resist the homogenization of these styles into one glutinous mass, many of the British fans decided firmly that Tex Mex, Cajun or Western Swing were definitely *not* Country. They sat firmly in the Jim Reeves, Charley Pride, Crystal Gayle anodyne corner, with Alabama, an atrociously processed Southern soft-rock band, romping home repeatedly as Country band of the Year . . . On the other hand cultured middle-class Brits who had previously felt equivocal about declaring any interest in something as trashy as C & W started to come out of the closet. Hank would be approached by smartly suited TV executives who would boldly whisper in his ear that they had always been big Loretta Lynn fans anyway . . .

Meantime, while he was filming in Nashville, Hank had his knuckles rapped for even calling it C & W.

'We don't call it Country and *Western* any more, that's kind of archaic now,' a television producer told him tetchily. 'As a matter of fact, we don't like to call it *Country* as it happens. Too old fashioned. We like to call it *American* music.' Hank reeled at this bit of nonsense. The implication was all too clear. The Nashville establishment was busy biting the hand that had fed it all those years in a final attempt to clear away the unacceptable, white-trash, hillbilly roots and produce a bland, easy-listening, *adult*, Las Vegas-bound kind of music. These were the same scheming opportunistic bastards, Hank thought, who had emasculated Elvis and taken the fire out of his Rock 'n' Roll. Well, they can just shove their American music up their American bottoms along with their phoney American sincerity, he said to himself, because we're going to *Keep It Country!*

In the end we survived Mrs Wigley and Potter Heigham but only just. And of course they never asked us back. So I wrote a song 'It Ain't Country Music':

It Ain't Country music, I know what I like,
And I know that I like what I know.
It ain't Country music, I know that I'm right
And if he can't play Jim Reeves, hoss,
Then he'll have to go . . .

Sam Hutt © $incere $ongs 1978

In the middle of the song's story of Mrs W's collapse in the face of the menacing bogey of Rock 'n' Roll, a doctor is brought in to examine her as she lies catatonic on the dance floor. *'It's Charley Prideitis,'* he says, *'there's one thing to do, Sing that Chandelier song and she's bound to pull through.'*

When we sang the song, at this point we would break into a therapeutic chorus of Crystal Chandeliers and everyone in whatever club we were playing would jump up and grab their partners, delighted to see that we were a real Country and Western band after all.

Cruelly, after only two lines of the chorus, just as everyone was beginning to shuffle blissfully round the floor I would scream *'No! That ain't Country music, I know what I like and I know that I like . . .'* and everyone would look as dazed as post-coital dogs and sit down. I tell you, it made me feel like a real shit at times. Hank made me do it. He kept saying it would be good for them. So whether Hank sang or I did, we were doing that song in the run up to the regional heats for the Mervyn Conn Best-of-British-Country competition which was to have its final at the Wembley bonanza.

*'The Human Hand is the greatest instrument of Shaking.' Mel Brooks.

The Full Wangford is a form of double-handed handshake perfected by Hank that combines both strength and sincerity. It has a suggestion of intimacy and a promise of friendliness with absolutely no sexual overtones. It is safe but firm. As the right hand is engaged in the normal business of handshaking with the right hand of the shakee, the left hand grips round the shakee's right elbow. The elbow is cupped in the hand, with the fingers curled into the inside of the arm. This is a soft and delicate part of the body and normally sensitive to the lightest touch. It should be squeezed gently but not suggestively. Rhythmic pumplike squeezes are not recommended.

The effect of the Full Wangford is immediately calming. It is friendly, reassuring and trustworthy. It is the most sincere of all known handshakes.

President Reagan was one of the great exponents of the Full Wangford. Watch him in action.

The Semi-Wangford is merely, as here, gripping the elbow alone in a soothingly authoritative way or, with the handshake, gripping merely the right hand or wrist of the shakee and not slipping up to the elbow. Hank maintains that this is not as effective and nothing like going all the way with the Full Wangford.

In a rare emergency, an exceptional case when the shakee does not respond or is overtly aggressive, it has the added advantage of complete immobilization of the right arm and shoulder and therefore at the same time the entire body. Should it be unfortunately necessary, the shakee can be anchored solidly in the Full Wangford as a brisk knee is delivered sharply and efficiently to the lower abdomen.

He'll Have to Go

Our heat was at Filby, back on the Norfolk Broads not a cowpat's throw from the Wigley ranch. The heartland again. It was in a pub's big music room right by a caravan park. In that part of the world, everything is beside a caravan park. I was there and watched Hank and the Wangs romp home. Most of the judges were journalists on the Country scene who had endured rather than enjoyed years of dreary British Country bands churning out carbon copies of American Country hits with as much inspiration as a trouser press. The Wangfords were a bit ramshackle, not the most technically brilliant band, but had an excitement and originality that was new to the scene. It must be said that there always have been, in among the dross, several good Country artists this side of the great water. I'd always rated Ray Lynam and Philomena Begley, who stood out from the then burgeoning Irish showband scene, as the George Jones and Tammy Wynette of Ireland. Recently Lynam has made the jump from the showband scene, getting himself a hard, new band and showing Country and Rock fans what a great singer he is. I'd also admired Philomena for staying with Begley rather than becoming Loretta Parton or something.

So the word got out that there was a whacky new band on the Country scene, more honkytonk than bluegrass, with shades of Gram Parsons, Commander Cody and latterly the Joe Ely band from Texas. By the time Wembley came around the Wangfords had become for many the Great White Hope. They were going to vitalize the torpid British Country scene, to show the way for the future. Hank got quite carried away with the idea of leading his Israelites through the desert of the Potter Heighams, the Red Sea of Wembley and on to a great and glorious future.

I was much more cynical about it all and told him not to be such a blockhead and certainly not to expect miracles. But Hank's stupid sentimentality has often led him into a few unnecessary scrapes and he wouldn't listen to a word.

When Easter came we'd fixed up another gig to help with the expenses of bringing the Wangmobile to London. Though it was only a support, it *was* in London, and it was at the incongruously named Nashville Rooms. Standing on a corner of one of the great western arteries out of London, bumper-to-bumper traffic spewing out of town past its doors day and night, the Nashville was not really much like its namesake in Tennessee. Opposite, on the other side of the six streaming lanes, was Curry in Hurry, the least inviting name for an Indian restaurant I've seen. I've never been in enough of a hurry to risk it. Besides, the traffic never stopped long enough to get across the road.

Inside, the Nashville was just another dirty old pub with a music room in the back, but it was one of the big venues on the London pub Rock circuit. Ironically it had been on the C & W circuit years before and an old acoustic guitar sitting in a glass case high up out of drunken reach, on the wall by the gent's pisser, was supposed to have belonged to the great Hank Williams. Oh, yeah?

Whether it did or not, ol' Hank's spirit looked after the Wangs the night they played there. They were supporting the Rezillos, a good, loud, thrashing punky band from Scotland. Their media-wise lead singers Fay Fife and Eugene Reynolds were like cartoon characters and were NME flavour of the moment. It was '78, in the mid-punk period and gobbing, phlegm tributes spat on stage, was in full swing. I worried for Hank.

In the long corridor of a dressing-room the Wangfords were getting more and more nervous. The Rezillos were at the other end of the dressing corridor having Very Important Rockbiz discussions very intensely and not a little self-importantly, totally oblivious to the Wangs. Hank thought they were unfriendly tossers but I told him that no one ever wants to talk to the support group. One of the most thankless tasks in the music business, doing the support. No one wants to talk to you, the audience don't want to listen to you, which is probably just as well because no one gives you a sound check and the man on the PA makes sure that you sound a lot worse than the stars.

Outside, waiting for some action, there were a lot of spiky tops, bondage trousers, chains, safety-pins, Doc Martens, bumflaps and black leather-studded jackets and no one knew what was going to happen. The closest thing to C & W in the Nashville that night was the Mohican haircuts. But Country and Western certainly wasn't the closest thing to the Mohicans. This was a different class of blockhead.

Though he was scared, Hank said before they went on that he still liked playing to an unknown audience, when everything wasn't safe and simple. He liked seeing what happened 'when the shit hit the fans' but still worried how headbangers would cope with Merle Haggard. When he came on he looked a bit edgy and the shouts of 'fuck off' didn't help too much. The band honky-tonked straight into 'Empty Bottle' and the noise from the crowd grew. Two punters right on my shoulder got stuck in straight away.

'Fuck off you Cunts. FUUUCCCK OOOFFFF! Fucking Bollocks.'

'BOOLLLLLOCCCCCKSSS!!!'

You get the picture. Not big honky-tonk fans.

But the Wangs banged on, driven by the Commander, Kirby, on drums and Roy on bass. Susie Cruise seemed to take charge early on and wasn't going to be worried by a bunch of punks. She'd handled worse in her stripping days and the rowdy crowd just fired her up.

'Now you boys just fuck off yourselves,' she harangued them between numbers. 'Watch your language and don't you arseholes forget there's a lady present.'

The punks roared and the band lurched into their Prairie version of the Troggs' classic 'Wild Thing'. Hank had heard it played this way when he toured round the States with the Evolent Brothers, Ben and Mal, in 1973. The punter by my left arm was still shouting when suddenly someone pushed him and he staggered into me.

'Shut your mouth and listen, all right?' I heard a growling voice from behind him say. The guy shut up. Susie had got her tenor sax out and was doing the business on it. She was very blowsy and rude on stage and didn't care who noticed. She was honking away, ravaging the audience with a good, rasping tenor solo. She *was* Wild Thing.

That was the point the Wangfords got them. From then on it was easy. The punks started slamming into each other on the honky-tonk numbers, gobbing on 'Cowboys Stay on Longer' and pogoing to the polkas. The Wangs cruised on through to the end of the set.

Backstage, the Rezillos were still discussing record deals and percentages and didn't notice us. Fair enough. Suddenly the door broke open and in came half a dozen punks.

'Fuckin' brilliant.'

'Yeah, that was great. Fuckin' all right.'

'Yeah, I fought you was great. I fought you was fuckin' rubbish to start wiv though, and I was shoutin' bollocks and shite and all that. But nah, you wasn't bad, as it 'appens, not bad at all. In fact you was fuckin' brill, mate, brill. Right.'

☆ ★ ☆

So by the time the Wangfords got to Wembley two days later they were really cocky. What with getting the punks pogoing and being a dead cert to win the Best of British finals, they felt unstoppable. A precarious certainty. Very dodgy. It's deadly to be a dead cert.

Feeling his blood surging, Hank decided to put 'It Ain't Country Music' into the three-number set. He still had the foolish fire of a crusade burning in his heart, the Great White Hope story had gone to his head a bit and he wanted to lay the old order of C & W to rest. Maybe he thought it was a political act. Maybe he was just a wally. I like to think he just didn't want to win.

The Wangfords came onstage at the Wembley Conference Centre ready to make history. Hank was incredibly Sincere, holding a mirror up to the Wembley style of cynical and ingratiating sincerity that he loved and hated so much. His own personal homage.

They opened confidently with 'You Turned Me On', which rattled along well and had everybody's toes tapping. And then Hank, knowing full well what he was doing, stuck his head right in the noose.

By singing the story of Mrs Wigley Hank committed Country and Western hara-kiri.

It was early on in the day and all but one of the judges lined up sitting at tables in front of the stage for that section of the competition were proprietors of C & W clubs . . . Just like the Bar H or Potter Heigham . . . 'It Ain't Country Music, I Know What I Like and I know that . . . Hmmm' . . . But Hank didn't know this, though he maintains that he would have done the song anyway.

'You have to let them know where you stand and what you're thinking, that's what Country music is about,' he says. 'You can't hide what you feel so what the hell. It's heart on the sleeve time. No other way.'

By the middle of the song, as Mrs W. is foaming and contorting on the floor and the doc is diagnosing Charley Prideitis, the judges to a man appeared to draw their pens in an identical diagonal line right across the scoresheet in front of them and push the sheets away. That was that. They paid no attention to 'Cowboys Stay On Longer', for why should they? They'd heard rumours before, that Hank was not *on their side*, that some Country clubs didn't even think he played C & W, that he was not to be trusted, that he was taking the piss out of Country, that he was some kind of dangerous heretic. And here was the proof.

Hank wasn't too downcast. He began to see that Wembley wasn't a world he belonged in and it was best not to pretend. It was becoming clear that Rock 'n' Rollers were far less narrow minded than the Country fans and it looked like Hank was going to pull the Rockers into his Health and Happiness show much more easily than show the Country mob that there was life after Jim Reeves.

☆ ★ ☆

So at last the C & W gigs started to fall away and if there was any sense of a crusade, it was more to play Country music to Rock audiences. Paradoxically Hank began to get more disinterested and I was standing in for him more and more of the time. He kept disappearing, going off further afield than Southwold, and seemed to be trying to confront some of his demons. How successful he was I can't say, for he kept turning up at Bulcamp House looking dishevelled and smelling strongly of booze. He appeared to be coming seriously unstuck and I figured that he would probably fall apart if we let him back on stage. So I prevailed and told him that I was handling the gigs for the time being, and that he needed the rest.

You look dangerously like you're trying to write ol' Hank out of this book. Worse still, you're trying to write yourself in.

No, Colonel, I'm just saying what happened as it happened.

Just don't turn Hank around, Doc. You make him sound pretty sick, but you're not too healthy yourself. And remember, I'm Hank's manager. Everything goes through me. And I'm still watching you.

In the last half of the Seventies Country was the least popular form of music to all but the diehard C & W faction. Yet we started to get more gigs in the London Rock pubs, and audiences new to Country found themselves liking it for the first time. We were asked back to the Nashville for our own headlining gigs where the great B. J. Cole played with us, beefing up the band with the massive sound he put out on his pedal steel. We played the now defunct Red Cow, where Susie Cruise brought the cancan girls who had danced at the first gig at the Horse Fair two years before. But the first London gig we did on our own was down in the little sweaty cellar at the Hope & Anchor – the Grope and Wanker – in Islington, which had seen the start of many great British Rock 'n' Rollers, from Nick Lowe and Graham Parker to Elvis Costello.

I was handling the bookings and doing all the agency work at this time. Colonel Frank Wangford had taken very much a back seat ever since Hank turned up in England to find his roots. In fact we never saw hide nor hair of the Colonel and from what Hank said there was little love lost between them. Hank had blamed the Colonel's monumental greed and appalling business ineptitude for his American decline. The Colonel had of course thrown it back at Hank's lack of staying power.

'If you can't stand the heat,' he'd muttered, 'stay out of the microwave.'

It was a waste of his talent to come back to look after Hank in his re-entry into the small time. Too much work for too little money, he'd said, and waited to see if Hank would make anything of his trip back home and establish himself in Britain or whether he'd ultimately go back to the States for another bite at the great maggoty apple. Hank hadn't had too much success in his last two years in the States, so he stayed this side of the great water.

In fact we saw less and less of ol' Hank straight after the Wembley fiasco and from June of that year I was doing all his gigs. I found the fake American accent the hardest part but got the hang of it after a while. But however well I did, the heart had somehow dropped out of the band with Hank's demise. Although we were coming down to London in the Wangmobile more often and doing better and higher profile gigs than the Bar H or the Queen's Head, Saxmundham, morale was low. Even playing with B. J., who was talking of recording us on his projected new British Country label Cowpie, didn't boost us enough. Six months after Wembley, in the autumn of '78, Susie left. Shortly after, Roy / Paul, who was musically and spiritually my right-hand man since Hank had gone, and the only remaining original member, said he'd had enough.

I took it badly. I wasn't as experienced as Hank, who had last been sighted busking in Morocco in the great square, in Marrakech. I had never held a full band together for any length of time before and took the break up personally. In my heart I couldn't let it go and realise that people had to do what they want and cannot be forced into anything. My reaction was every bit as selfish and self-indulgent as it had been before, as if I had learnt nothing in the intervening years or from my contact with Hank.

I went into a decline. I left Suffolk and got blacker and blacker. One day I fell down some stairs on my way to an Arsenal game; being an Arsenal supporter and dealing with their depressingly defensive and often boring play was always at the very least character forming. Everybody who wasn't a supporter also hated and despised you for following Arsenal, it seemed, more than any other team. Their reputation for being stinking rich, élitist, top heavy, dull and uninspiring is difficult to shift.

But for an Arsenal supporter things are always looking a little brighter, the good times are just round the corner. It's like the Highlanders looking out over the Skye skies for a patch of slightly lighter grey that could promise an end to the unremitting drizzle . . . 'Aye, it's looking a wee bit brighter just over there' . . . And I found it especially therapeutic in those dark days to go up on a grey winter day to Highbury, and however bad I felt, to see that things could always be worse. Especially by falling down the stairs on the way to a game.

After years of bending and twisting my elongated spine in a totally unergonomic way over an examining couch at family planning clinics, the fall down the stairs and the three hours standing in the cold on the

North Bank terrace did the trick. Next morning I woke up in agony and couldn't move. I'd got a severe slipped disc and was bed ridden for the next two months. I plunged further into depression and thought I'd be crippled for life. When it takes half an hour to get from lying on the back to sitting on the side of the bed, you know you're in a bad way. And when it doesn't get any better from week to week you start to panic that that's it. All over. No more nothing.

I've rarely suffered from guilt, but when I was a kid and discovered the surreptitious joys of masturbation, I was convinced during a very brief religious period that the pimples that were bursting all over my face were a punishment from God, who could see everywhere, even into my bathroom. So I'd go round to the local church and put money in the collection box at the gate to see if the acne would go away without having to stop playing with my new stiff little toy. I tried to buy God off, but it didn't work.

In the same retrogressive way, as I lay immobile flat on my back, I thought God was telling me something. As He had attacked me in the lower back I figured He was telling me that I have been too obsessed with sex. That I was confusing Love and Sex, that sex was a red herring. The sort of things we said in psychosexual seminars. Maybe I should concentrate on higher things.

I guess I was just depressed. Easy enough if you are on your own, the band has broken up, and day after day, week after week, the pain gets no better and movement remains well nigh impossible. With Hank gone it looked like I'd never perform again. Half-way through my thirties, I was having my first and only mid-life crisis.

Gradually it lifted. I found I could make love gently and I found I could start to get out of bed, however gingerly. And then B. J. Cole came round to say he definitely wanted to make a Wangford album, and that he could organise the musos to do it with us.

Things were looking up.

Good Loud Country

During the brutally Orwellian year of 1984, I had to show that I stood with the miners in their struggle. My sympathies had been with them ever since I was a kid staying with my Aunt Jean in Glasgow's Provanmill.

> **Hold on there, Doc. Not giving away too many freebies, are you?**
> Just a trailer, Colonel. Something to whet their appetites.
> **OK, just a taste, then. But what has this got to do with Hank?**
> I've told you before, Colonel, by this time I hadn't seen Hank
> for over two years and I was standing in for him all the time.
> **Oh, right, right. And you still weren't drinking?**
> Why should I be, Hank did enough of that for both of us.
> **Fine. Well, give us your little trailers, then.**

Our next-door neighbours in Glasgow were nearly all Catholics. Sissy Macartney and her seven children were Catholics but Bill, the father, who had been a miner all his life, was a Communist. It got very heated in the Macartney home when Bill got pissed. After years down the pits, his lungs were completely rotten and clogged with coal, and seriously weakened by them, he used to get pissed easily. He was a small man, with a lot of difficulty breathing, but pissed he became a giant. He'd clamber on to a chair, sway glassily, steady himself with his arm round my shoulder and, wheezing away and coughing up black phlegm, he would shout in solidarity into my ear.

'C'mon, Sam, youse an' me, let's sing "The British Workin' Man" and tae hell wi' yon Papists.'

'Och, ssh, Bill, remember the Virgin Mary . . .' As Bill was the

164

only Communist, everybody else in the room would be crossing themselves wildly with one hand and shushing the old man with the other.

'Holy Mary Mother of God, please forgive him . . . oh Bill, you shouldnae say that aboot the Virgin Mary!'

'Och, fuck the Virgin Mary, c'mon, Sam, let's sing "The Red Flag". "The People's Flag is deepest red . . ."' Cough . . . splutter . . .

Bill was invalided early out of the pits – his lungs were solid with dust – but didn't get the full disability pension. After medical examination it was claimed that he didn't have *Pneumoconiosis*, very pensionable, but had *Silicosis*. Sorry mate, I'd love to help you, really I would, but my hands are tied. The difference is that Pneumoconiosis has a high proportion of coal dust and Silicosis a high proportion of stone dust. Rockier coal has more Silica in it than softer coal. Hairs were being cruelly split. Both conditions, whatever the proportion of coal to stone, result in a destructive fibrosis of lung tissue which stops you breathing. You drown in your own lungs. And after a lifetime given to the coal which retired him early and after being exploited even in his retirement, Bill Macartney finally stopped breathing. So for Bill's sake I had to show solidarity. This wasn't the first time the Wangfords were on the losing side, but that's Country music for you.

ON THE LINE

Back in the summer of '84
We tried to help the miners win their war.
We came to do a gig for the GLC –
That's Good Loud Country for you and me.
We came for music and now and then
For words of wisdom from old Red Ken
Who said 'Three million people are unemployed
The heart of a nation is being destroyed'

NO ONE KNOWS YOU WHEN YOU'RE ON THE LINE
THEY ALL WANT TO HELP YOU WHEN YOU'RE DOING FINE.

There were hippies and punks and OAPs
UB 40s and CIDs
But no one noticed them bad bad boys
With the bottles and the skins and the mouthful of noise.
'Cos they slipped through the crowd like a shiver of fear,
With them Air Wair steps that you never can hear.
And I knew what they were when I saw them salute
And they knew I was a Commie from my flash pink suit.

NO ONE KNOWS YOU . . .

We started to polka and they went 'Seig Heil'
They jumped us and polka'd on our faces for a while
They knocked us down and put in the boot,
Made a real mess of my flash pink suit.
They smashed a guitar, jagged like a knife,
And cut into the face of my friend for life.
'N there was no one to stop them, no security,
From the police or the crowd or the GLC.

No one told us while Billy Bragg sing
That the Redskins just had the boot put in.
No one warned us before we went on
A hundred to one we wouldn't finish our song.

NO ONE KNOWS YOU WHEN YOU'RE ON THE LINE
THEY ALL WANT TO HELP YOU WHEN YOU'RE DOING FINE.
NO ONE KNOWS YOU WHEN YOU'RE ON THE LINE.

Don't Rob Another
☆
Man's Castle

We teetered into the Eighties. Hank was getting increasingly depressed as I was surfacing from my dark patch. We had seesawed emotionally like that ever since we met properly in Wangford four years earlier. As he picked me up and I got out of my self-imposed heartache he started to sink. Now that I was stronger and my back was working better than it had done for a while, he was falling away again, stumbling, going wobbly. In the middle of all this, in spite of himself, he became Born Again, and somehow he found God. Unfortunately, God didn't stop his battle with the bottle. It was here he wrote 'Big G' which he was singing as we set up the recording session with B. J. We had to include it on the album.

BIG G

Now I got religion pretty late in life,
'Bout the time I broke up with my third ex-wife,
My friend was a bottle, my life was a lie,
And I couldn't believe in that Pie in the Sky, or

BIG G,
HE'S BIGGER THAN YOU AND HE'S BIGGER THAN ME
HE'S BETTER THAN A SMOKE OR A CUP OF TEA

HE'S THE ONE TO SET YOU FREE
BIG G
BIG G

I was hitting the bottle, out on the streets,
In my cardboard bed with my newspaper sheets.
I thought I was just about as low as I could get
When a voice like rumbling thunder said, Boy,
You ain't seen nothing yet,
That was BIG G . . .

Now before I saw the light I was a miserable slave
I thought I was alive but I was dancing in my grave
Now I've got the Man beside me, I ain't scared to die
I'll join that holy roadshow, play my guitar in the sky

With BIG G,
HE'S BIGGER THAN YOU AND HE'S BIGGER THAN ME
HE'S BETTER THAN A SMOKE OR A CUP OF TEA
BIG G
BIG G . . .

© Bucks Music and $incere $ongs

I wrote liner notes for the album. David Oxtoby did the front cover, a fine picture of me looking a bit like Clint Eastwood with a nose job that had gone wrong and a tear in my eye for my lost friend. In the background Hank, with his old moustache, was looming and melancholy. It perfectly summed up this whole time.

Although Hank never turned up for any of the recordings after the planning stage and I had to sing lead vocals in his place, I was convinced he was going to turn up again sometime.

As I said on the back of the album:

'Pain is where Country Music is at,' Hank used to say, 'you have to have your hands in a bowl of dishwater to really feel it.'

And I tell you, he really felt it. After honky-tonkin' from Texas to Wisconsin . . . he came back to England disillusioned with the reek of insincere sincerity in Country Music.

So I met the High Priest of Pain, was ravaged by his clammy perception of truth, and joined his band. Recently his depression deepened, he wrote his hauntingly prophetic 'Big G' and . . . disappeared in the middle of doing the backing tracks for this album. I've put a couple of mine on here but I'm sure Hank won't mind.

But this is not an obituary. Hank may have slipped away awhile, beat feet down some tumbling track, but I don't think he's dead. That's not Hank's style. The Wangford Hall of Pain hasn't locked its doors yet, and there's a whole stack of dishes left to wash.

No, it wasn't an obituary and the record wasn't his epitaph. He had to come back. He couldn't stay depressed for ever.

That's better, Doc. We don't want to think Hank has gone for ever. It keeps looking like you're trying to push him aside.

No, Colonel, I'm just standing in for him.

Yes, yes, but ... C'mon Doc, you can tell me ... He's not around a lot these days is he?

Well, he turned up the time we did the 'A to Z of C & W' series for TV.

Oh, sure, a free trip to the States and cheap booze.

Oh, come off it, Colonel, that's crap. He's a difficult man. Sometimes it's hard for him to cope. Sometimes we have to cope for him. OK, I did half that TV series after he vanished into the Texas night down in San Antonio. But I'm still only standing in.

Listen, Doc, let's not beat around the bush. Sometimes I think you do Hank as well as Hank himself. Now I don't want to waste your time or mine. I'm prepared to offer you a unique contract, a real special deal. I'll even put your cut up to ... *sixty per cent.* **How else can I say it?**

Colonel, please.

You're a *registered* **doctor, right? There must be a way we can classify the show as medical – good tax concessions.**

Colonel ...

Or how would you feel about a lecture tour?

Colonel, no disrespect, but do you see that microphone?

What, that one in the corner there?

Yes. That microphone standing there is Hank's mike.

Hank's?

Yes. I use my own, but I'm keeping his for when he comes back. After all, if you think about it *sincerely*, Colonel, you must admit that it is still Hank's gig. So let's have no talk of signing contracts right now. Hank was around a lot in the Eighties, and we haven't seen the last of him yet. We're just caretakers. Let's just take care.

Here are a few pointers for you folks who haven't heard any good Country but want to. It's not definitive, but it's a taste that should set you up right.

Some favourite records:
Lefty Frizzell 'His Life, His Music' vol.7 (Bear Family Records)
George Jones 'Sings Bob Wills & Hank Williams' (United Artists)
George Jones 'Burn the Honky-Tonk Down' (Rounder Records)
George Jones 'Heartaches and Hangovers' (Rounder Records)
George Jones 'The Best of . . .' (Epic)
George Jones & Tammy Wynette 'Best of . . .' (Epic)
Louvin Brothers 'My Baby's Gone' (Stetson)
Louvin Brothers 'Tragic Songs of Life' (Rounder Records)
Blue Sky Boys 'Sunny Side of Life' (Rounder Records)
Gram Parsons 'Grievous Angel' with Emmylou Harris (Reprise/WEA)
Flying Burrito Brothers 'Gilded Palace of Sin' (A&M/DEMON)
Merle Haggard 'Best of . . .' (Capital/MCA)
Dolly Parton, Emmylou Harris & Linda Ronstadt 'Trio' (WEA)
Hank Williams Sr '20 Greatest Hits' (Polygram)
Conway Twitty & Loretta Lynn 'Best of . . .' (MCA)
Conway Twitty & Loretta Lynn 'Lead Me On' (MCA)
Joe Ely 'Honky-Tonk Masquerade' (MCA)
Hank Wangford 'Bumper Box' (Cowpie Records)
Randy Travis 'Storm of Life' (WEA)
Nashville Bluegrass Band 'To Be His Child' (Rounder Records)
Willie Nelson 'Red Headed Stranger' (CBS)
Willie Nelson 'Greatest Hits' (CBS)
Dolly Parton 'Best of . . .' (RCA)

There are lots more!

The best book to tell you all about Country music through the records is *The Best of Country Music* John Morthland (Doubleday, NY 1984). It is opiniated and sharp as a needle.

Also there is the *Illustrated Encyclopaedia of Country Music*, Fred Dellar, Alan Cackett, Roy Thompson (Salamander).

A good reference is *Country Music USA*, Bill C. Malone (University of Texas).

Your Cheatin' Heart about Hank Williams is a controversial fictionalized biography of Hank which is very readable.

The Country Music Federation have brought out the definitive *Country* with the best sets of pictures around.

Country! by Nick Tosches may all be lies but it's a good read.

Hellfire is about Jerry Lee Lewis, the perfect example of the Great Contradiction in Country.